by
Donald Jacobs
and
August Treff

AGS®
American Guidance Service, Inc.
Circle Pines, Minnesota 55014-1796

About the Authors

Donald H. Jacobs earned his masters degree from Johns Hopkins University and is currently teaching high school mathematics in the Baltimore City public school system. He has served as the coordinator of computer programming at the Talmudical Academy of Baltimore. Mr. Jacobs also was a member of the writing team for the BASIC programming curriculum for Baltimore City schools.

August V. Treff is currently a Divisional Specialist in Research and Evaluation with Baltimore City public schools. He has worked as a consultant for the Maryland State Department of Education to develop the functional mathematics manual. He has also served as a consultant for ESEA Chapter 1 elementary math instruction. Mr. Treff earned his masters degree from Loyola College.

Consultant
Ken Levine
Mathematics Teacher
Baltimore County Public Schools
Baltimore, Maryland

Staff
Donna Babylon, Senior Editor
Mary D. Szarek, Editor
Beth Hornung Bill, Contributing Editor
Norm Myers, Design
Lynna Bright, Typesetting, Graphics, and Layout
Carol Munschauer, Art

Printed in the United States of America.
ISBN: 0-88671-522-9 (Previously ISBN: 0-7916-0085-8)

Order Number: 80070
A 0 9 8 7 6 5

CONTENTS

CHAPTER 1

COUNTING CALORIES

WHAT IS A CALORIE?

Do you like to eat? Most people do! Your body needs food in order to grow and to stay healthy. The *nutrients* in your food provide energy for your body. Some foods provide more energy than others. This energy is measured in calories.

A *calorie* is the amount of energy needed to raise the temperature of 1000 *grams* of water one degree *Celsius*. An active person needs to *consume* more calories than a quiet person. A large person needs more calories than a small person.

Many people count the calories contained in the food that they eat when they are trying to gain or lose weight. Some people also count the calories their bodies burn when they exercise.

If you are to count calories, you will need to add and subtract whole numbers. The answer to an addition problem is called the *sum*. The answer to a subtraction problem is called the *difference*. Try these problems to check your skills.

Examples:

Add: 325 + 1238 + 428

```
   325
  1238
+  428
_____
  1991    Sum
```

Subtract: 436 from 2574

```
  2574
-  436
_____
  2138    Difference
```

EXERCISE A.   Find the sums and differences.

1) 345 + 2428	11) 5007 - 344
2) 4628 - 732	12) 1463 - 729
3) 3657 - 246	13) 98 + 243 + 605
4) 325 + 468 + 1105	14) 734 + 825 + 616
5) 4638 - 706	15) 4235 - 789
6) 625 + 752 + 308	16) 1256 - 908
7) 1240 + 623 + 752	17) 128 + 624 + 392 + 428
8) 3005 - 638	18) 1763 - 398
9) 1563 + 1238 + 673	19) 2035 - 1742
10) 461 + 1063 + 736	20) 802 + 1036 + 250 + 109

ADDING CALORIES

This chart shows that different foods have different amounts of calories.

Calorie Values of Common Foods	
Food	**Calories**
Hot dog with roll	280
Hamburger with roll	370
Mayonnaise, 1 tbsp.	110
French fries	155
Chocolate milk, 1 cup	190
Cola, 1 cup	105
Chocolate candy bar	145

We can find out how many calories are in several foods by adding. For example, Mike went to a fast food restaurant for lunch. He had a hamburger with a roll and a cup of chocolate milk. How many calories did he consume in all? Use the chart above to add the calories. (The total calories Mike consumed was 560.)

Solution: Add to find the total.

Hamburger with roll	370	Calories
Chocolate milk, 1 cup	+ 190	Calories
	560	Total

EXERCISE A. Find the total number of calories of other customers' meals ordered at the same restaurant.

1) John asked for a hot dog and a cola.
2) Maria ordered a hamburger with mayonnaise and French fries.
3) José wanted a hot dog, French fries, chocolate milk, and a chocolate candy bar.

Calorie Values of Fruit Servings

Applesauce, 1 cup	230
Banana	120
Blackberries, 1 cup	85
Fruit cocktail, 1 cup	195
Orange	65
Peach	40
Pear	100
Plum, large	33
Raspberries, 1 cup	70

EXERCISE B.   Use the chart above. Find the answers to these questions by adding the calories together.

1) Chris ate a banana, a peach, and an orange. How many calories did he consume?

2) Alan had three plums and a pear. How many calories were in the fruit?

3) Lee fixed himself a cup of applesauce for breakfast and a cup of fruit cocktail for lunch. How many calories did he eat?

4) How many calories are in two cups of applesauce?

5) How many calories are in two oranges and a pear?

6) Sue decided to make her own fruit cocktail for her friends. She used one orange, one banana, two peaches, and two cups of raspberries. What was the total calorie count for this fruit cocktail?

7) How many calories are in two bananas, a peach, and two plums?

8) Kim mixed one cup of blackberries with one cup of fruit cocktail. What is the total number of calories?

Here are the calorie values of some of the foods served at a local restaurant.

Item	Calories
Chicken drumstick	90
Fish, breaded, fried	280
Hamburger steak, 6 oz.	270
Liver, fried, 6 oz.	390
Steak, lean, 6 oz.	660
Beets	65
Black-eyed peas	220
Broccoli	50
Corn, creamed	210
Mixed vegetables	115
Potato, baked	95
Rice	201
Butter, 1 tbsp.	100
Milk, whole, 1 cup	150
Milk, chocolate, 1 cup	210
Cola, 12 oz.	145
Root beer, 12 oz.	150

EXERCISE C.   Use the chart above. Find the total calorie value of each person's meal by adding the calories together.

1)   Jimmy chose a drumstick, creamed corn, rice, and a cola. How many calories were in his dinner?

2)   Bruce piled his plate with a lean steak, fried liver, black-eyed peas, a baked potato, and butter. Then he drank a cup of whole milk. What was the total calorie count of his meal?

3)   Janie enjoyed fried fish, broccoli, rice, and a root beer. How many calories were in her meal?

EXERCISE D.   Count the total calories for each of these meals. Use the chart on page 5.

1)   Fried liver
     Corn
     Baked potato
     Chocolate milk

2)   Chicken drumstick
     Rice
     Beets
     Root beer

3)   Hamburger steak
     Mixed vegetables
     Baked potato
     Butter
     Cola

4)   Fish
     Black-eyed peas
     Rice
     Whole milk

5)   Lean steak
     Broccoli
     Rice
     Butter
     Root beer

6)   2 chicken drumsticks
     Baked potato
     Black-eyed peas
     Cola

7)   Fried liver
     Mixed vegetables
     Baked potato
     Butter
     Chocolate milk

8)   Lean steak
     Beets
     Creamed corn
     Rice
     Milk

9)   Fish
     Broccoli
     Baked potato
     Chocolate milk

10) Hamburger steak
     Black-eyed peas
     Rice
     Root beer

11) Chicken drumstick
     Mixed vegetables
     Baked potato
     Cola

12) Lean steak
     Broccoli
     Butter
     Rice
     Chocolate milk

SUBTRACTING CALORIES

Ron consumed 2900 calories on Monday. He exercised for one hour and his body used 522 calories. How many calories were not used? To find the answer, subtract the calories used from the calories consumed.

2900	Calories consumed
- 522	Calories used
2378	Calories not used (the difference)

EXERCISE A.   Find the answers to these questions by subtracting.

1) Fontana consumes an average of 2500 calories per day. If her body uses 250 calories in one hour of walking, how many calories remain?

2) Derek's average calorie intake is 3100 per day. His main exercise is lying on the beach, listening to the waves. If his body burned 95 calories doing this, how many calories were left unused?

Find the difference for each example.

3)   3350 calories consumed
       782 calories used

4)   3641 calories consumed
       395 calories used

5)   2963 calories consumed
       463 calories used

6)   2460 calories consumed
       868 calories used

ADDING OR SUBTRACTING CALORIES

Kyle Swenson is 16 years old. He needs 3600 calories each day to keep active and stay healthy.

The chart below shows what Kyle had for breakfast. It also shows the calorie value for each food.

Food	Calories
2 fried eggs	85 each
3 slices of bacon	104 each
2 slices nut bread	85 each
2 tbsp. butter	100 each
2 glasses of milk	124 each

How many calories did Kyle consume at breakfast? Add to find the total.

$$
\begin{array}{rl}
85 & \\
85 & \Big\}\ \text{Eggs} \\
104 & \\
104 & \Big\}\ \text{Bacon} \\
104 & \\
85 & \\
85 & \Big\}\ \text{Nut bread} \\
100 & \\
100 & \Big\}\ \text{Butter} \\
124 & \\
+\ 124 & \Big\}\ \text{Milk} \\
\hline
1100 & \text{Total}
\end{array}
$$

Kyle consumed 1100 calories at breakfast. How many more calories must Kyle have during the day to reach the required 3600 calories? Subtract to find the calories needed.

3600	Calories required
- 1100	Had at breakfast
2500	

Kyle needs to have 2500 more calories during the day.

This is what Kyle ate during the rest of that day:

	Food	Calories
Lunch:	2 pieces chicken	260 each
	1 baked potato	95
	1 slice bread	70
	1 tbsp. butter	100
	1 cola	145
Snack:	Potato chips	230
	Chocolate milkshake	355
Dinner:	Beef soup	120
	Roast beef, 9 oz.	490
	Rice	200
	Broccoli, cooked	50
	Carrots, raw	40
	2 glasses of milk	124 each

EXERCISE A. Answer the following questions. Add or subtract to find the answers.

1) How many calories did Kyle have at lunch?
2) How many calories were in his snack?
3) How many calories did Kyle have at dinner?
4) How many calories did he have during the entire day?

5) Was his total calorie count for the day less than 3600 or greater than 3600?

6) What was the difference between his total count and 3600?

7) For his snack, suppose that Kyle drank a glass of milk instead of a milkshake. By how much would he have lowered his calorie count?

8) If Kyle had skipped the bacon for breakfast, how much lower would his calorie count have been?

ESTIMATING CALORIES USED

It is easy for people to *increase* their calories. The more they eat, the more calories they add. However, it takes much more time and effort for your body to use calories.

The body gets a certain amount of energy from each calorie. The more active a person is, the faster he or she uses calories.

The *graph* below shows the number of calories that are used in one hour of activity. The amounts shown may *vary* from person to person depending on age, weight, and sex.

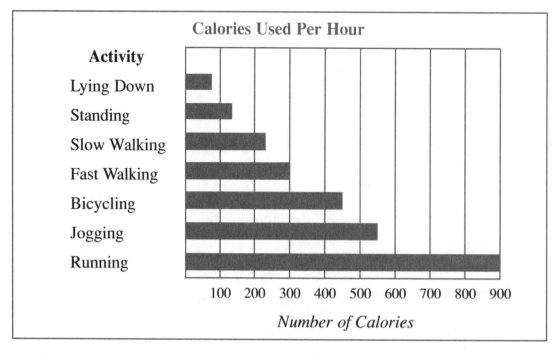

We may use the graph to *estimate*, or guess, needed information. For example, the number of calories used while walking slowly for one hour can be estimated from this chart. The bar for slow walking reaches past the 200 line. Since the end of the bar is closer to 200 than to 300, the estimate is 200 calories.

EXERCISE A.   Use the graph to estimate the number of calories used per hour for each of these activities.

1) Lying down   3) Standing   5) Jogging
2) Bicycling   4) Running   6) Fast walking

ADDING AND SUBTRACTING CALORIES

Below is a table that shows the number of calories used in an hour by different activities.

Calories Used in One Hour	
Activity	**Calories**
Sitting in class	100
Studying	105
Eating	125
Typing	140
Making beds	175
Washing dishes	180
Playing ping pong	230
Lifting weights	500

For example, Tom consumed 3295 calories one day. Then he typed for one hour and played ping pong for one hour. Find the number of calories not used.
First, you need to add the calories used:

140	Typing
+ 230	Playing ping pong
370	Calories used

Then, subtract the calories used from the calories consumed:

3295   Calories consumed
- 370   Calories used
―――――
2925   Calories not used

EXERCISE A.   Find the number of calories not used.

1)   Jim consumed 2935 calories. He spent one hour studying and one hour typing.

2)   Katie's calorie intake was 3255. She sat in class for one hour and studied for one hour.

3)   Mason consumed 2892 calories. He made beds for one hour and washed dishes for one hour.

4)   Ann Parks, an athlete, lifted weights for one hour. Then she ate a slow lunch for one hour. Her lunch totaled 962 calories.

5)   Lamont consumed 1932 calories. He spent one hour each on making beds, eating, and washing dishes.

Calculator Practice 1

A calculator can help you add numbers. Key in each number carefully. Then verify the number on the calculator display before you go on to the next number.

CALCULATOR EXERCISE.   Practice with a calculator. Add this list of calories to find each total.

265	120	50	923
423	460	23	1063
80	290	125	103
+ 293	+ 310	+ 62	+ 40

Computer Practice 1

A computer can be easy and fun to use. It can also help you to add. Remember to type the word PRINT before each set of numbers.
(See Appendix for more information.)

Example: Add 235 and 6211.

Type on the computer:

PRINT   235 + 6211

Then, press the RETURN or ENTER key. The answer, 6446, will appear on the screen.

COMPUTER EXERCISE.   Use a computer to add these numbers.

1)   380 + 4621

2)   9485 + 291

3)   3048 + 592

4)   3041 + 4058

5)   2938 + 284 + 398

6)   2033 + 1162 + 331

Food	Calories	One-Hour Activity	Calories Used
Hamburger steak	270	Baseball	360
Lean steak	660	Basketball	500
Chicken leg	90	Calisthenics	300
French fries	155	Gymnastics	430
Cola	105	Singing	135
Milk, 1 cup	150		

Use the information in the charts above to find the answer to each of these problems.

1) Alvaro chose a hamburger steak, French fries, and a cola for lunch. How many calories did he consume?

2) Eve had a lean steak, French fries, and two cups of milk. How many calories did she consume?

3) Cass needs 2435 calories each day. She had a chicken leg, French fries, and a cup of milk. How many more calories does she need?

4) Martha had a hamburger steak and a cola. Sue had a lean steak and a cup of milk. Find the difference in their calorie intake.

5) Joy played baseball and basketball for one hour each. How many calories did she use?

6) Lance did calisthenics for one hour and then did gymnastics for two hours. Find the total calories used.

Find the number of calories not used.

7) 2685 calorie intake with one hour of singing.

8) 3230 calorie intake with two hours of baseball.

9) 2900 calorie intake with two hours of gymnastics.

10) 3150 calorie intake with three hours of basketball.

CHAPTER 2

INTRODUCTION

Most home improvement projects involve using mathematics. In addition to measuring, you might need to multiply to find the *surface area* of the walls to be painted and the floor space to be carpeted.

When you multiply one whole number by another, begin by multiplying by the ones *digit*. Next, multiply by the tens digit. Be sure that you begin recording your *partial product* in the tens place. Start recording in the hundreds place when you multiply by the hundreds digit. The answer to a multiplication problem is called a *product*.

Examples:

$$
\begin{array}{r}
248 \\
\times\ \ 7 \leftarrow \text{Ones} \\
\hline
1736
\end{array}
\qquad
\begin{array}{r}
359 \\
\times\ \ 68 \leftarrow \text{Tens} \\
\hline
2\ 872 \\
21\ 58 \\
\hline
24{,}412
\end{array}
\qquad
\begin{array}{r}
137 \\
\times\ \ 146 \leftarrow \text{Hundreds} \\
\hline
822 \\
5\ 48 \\
13\ 7 \\
\hline
20{,}002
\end{array}
$$

EXERCISE A.   Solve these problems by multiplying.

1)   236
    ×   8

2)   529
    ×   6

3)   608
    ×   7

4)   537
    ×   4

5)   346
    ×   26

6)   503
    ×   75

7)   639
    ×   96

8)   398
    ×   62

9)   307
    × 563

10)   571
    × 402

11)   835
    × 118

12)   734
    × 237

Household activities also require the use of division, for example, to find the number of *square units* of carpet or the number of boxes of floor tile you need.

To divide one whole number by another, work from left to right. Place the digits in your answer over the last digit that you divide into. The answer to a division problem is called a *quotient*.

Examples:

Divide 7 into 37 tens. (The 5 goes above the 7 because it represents 5 tens.)
Divide 7 into 28 ones. (The 4 goes above the 8 because it represents 4 ones.)

```
      54
7 ) 378
    35
    ──
     28
     28
     ──
      0
```

Divide 28 into 118. The 4 goes over the 8.
Divide 28 into 63. The 2 goes over the 3.
Write any *remainder* over the *divisor*.

$$28\overline{)1183}$$

$$\begin{array}{r} 4 \\ 28\overline{)1183} \\ 112 \\ \hline 6 \end{array}$$

$$\begin{array}{r} 42\frac{7}{28} \\ 28\overline{)1183} \\ 112 \\ \hline 63 \\ 56 \\ \hline 7 \end{array} = 42\frac{1}{4}$$

EXERCISE B. Find the quotients. Write any remainders over the divisor.

1) $7\overline{)336}$

2) $6\overline{)282}$

3) $8\overline{)2104}$

4) $4\overline{)824}$

5) $12\overline{)816}$

6) $14\overline{)540}$

7) $11\overline{)3276}$

8) $13\overline{)1278}$

9) $28\overline{)476}$

10) $32\overline{)1090}$

11) $68\overline{)2312}$

12) $54\overline{)2268}$

13) $7\overline{)\$8.61}$

14) $4\overline{)\$9.52}$

15) $12\overline{)708}$

16) $14\overline{)\$4.48}$

PAINTING WALLS

When starting a project like painting walls, you will need to know the surface area of the walls before you can buy the paint. To find the area multiply the length and the height of each wall to be painted. Remember to subtract the area of any doors or windows. Area is measured in square units.

Example:

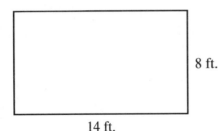

8 ft. × 12 ft. = 96 sq. ft.
7 ft. × 3 ft. = 21 sq. ft.
96 sq. ft. - 21 sq. ft. = 75 sq. ft.
75 square feet to be painted.

EXERCISE A. Find the surface area of each wall.

1)

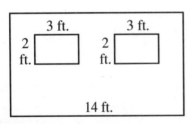

4)

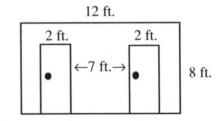

2)

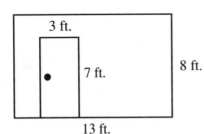

5)

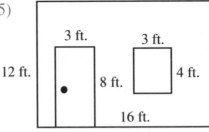

3)

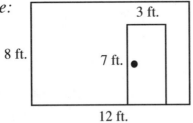

6)

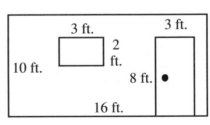

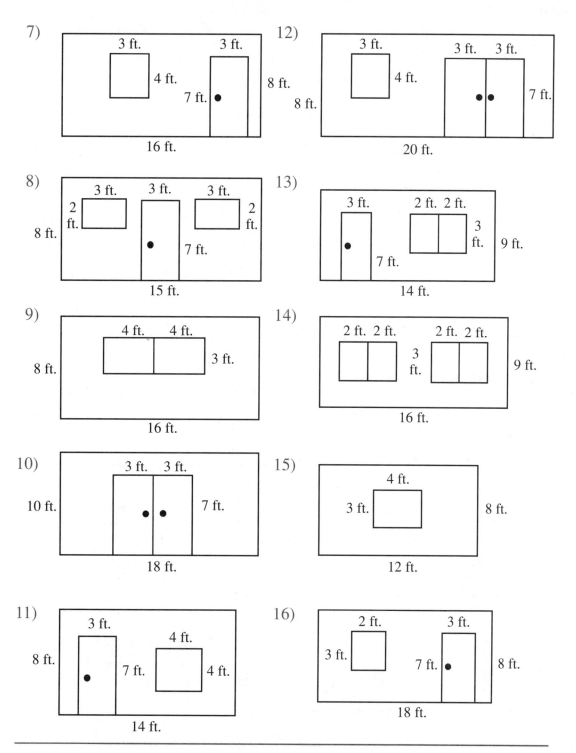

7)

3 ft.   3 ft.
4 ft.
7 ft. ●
8 ft.
16 ft.

12)

3 ft.   3 ft.   3 ft.
4 ft.
●●
8 ft.
8 ft.   7 ft.
20 ft.

8)

3 ft.   3 ft.   3 ft.
2 ft.   2 ft.
8 ft.   ●   7 ft.
15 ft.

13)

3 ft.   2 ft. 2 ft.
3 ft.   9 ft.
●   7 ft.
14 ft.

9)

4 ft.   4 ft.
3 ft.
8 ft.
16 ft.

14)

2 ft. 2 ft.   2 ft. 2 ft.
3 ft.   9 ft.
16 ft.

10)

3 ft.   3 ft.
10 ft.   ● ●   7 ft.
18 ft.

15)

4 ft.
3 ft.   8 ft.
12 ft.

11)

3 ft.
8 ft.   4 ft.
●   7 ft.   4 ft.
14 ft.

16)

2 ft.   3 ft.
3 ft.   7 ft. ●   8 ft.
18 ft.

An easy way to find the surface area of a room is to add the lengths of all of the walls. Then multiply the answer by the height of the room. Finally, subtract the area of any doors and windows.

Example:

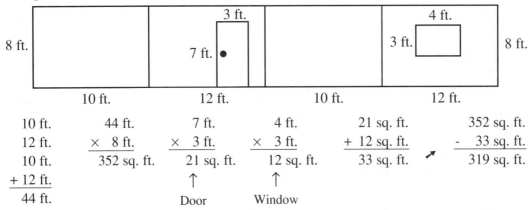

10 ft.	44 ft.	7 ft.	4 ft.	21 sq. ft.	352 sq. ft.
12 ft.	× 8 ft.	× 3 ft.	× 3 ft.	+ 12 sq. ft.	- 33 sq. ft.
10 ft.	352 sq. ft.	21 sq. ft.	12 sq. ft.	33 sq. ft.	319 sq. ft.
+ 12 ft.		↑	↑		
44 ft.		Door	Window		

There are 319 sq. ft. of surface area.

EXERCISE B.   Find the surface area of each of these rooms.

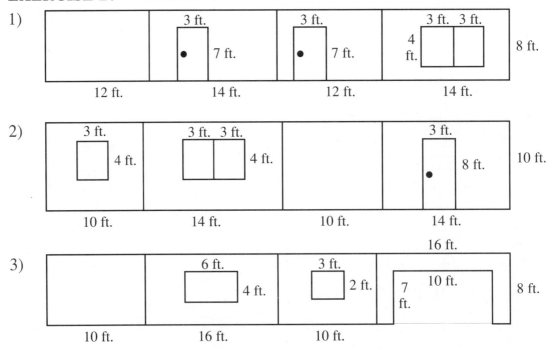

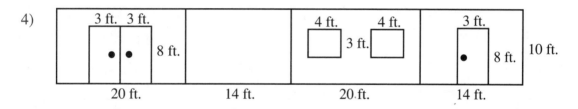

4)

| 3 ft. | 3 ft. | | 4 ft. | 4 ft. | 3 ft. |

20 ft.   14 ft.   20 ft.   14 ft.

DETERMINING CARPET AMOUNTS

Carpet is usually sold by the square yard in carpet stores. To find the number of square yards of carpet that you need, find the area of the floor in square feet. Divide this answer by 9. You divide by 9 because there are 9 square feet in one square yard.

Example:

Step 1:
$13 \times 11 = 143$ square feet.

Step 2:
$143 \div 9 = 15 \frac{8}{9}$

There are $15 \frac{8}{9}$ square yards.

EXERCISE A.   Find the number of square yards of carpet that are needed to carpet each floor drawn below.

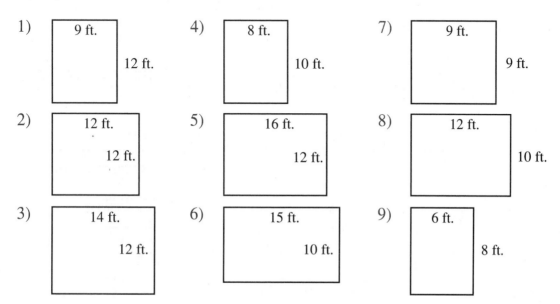

1)   9 ft.   12 ft.

2)   12 ft.   12 ft.

3)   14 ft.   12 ft.

4)   8 ft.   10 ft.

5)   16 ft.   12 ft.

6)   15 ft.   10 ft.

7)   9 ft.   9 ft.

8)   12 ft.   10 ft.

9)   6 ft.   8 ft.

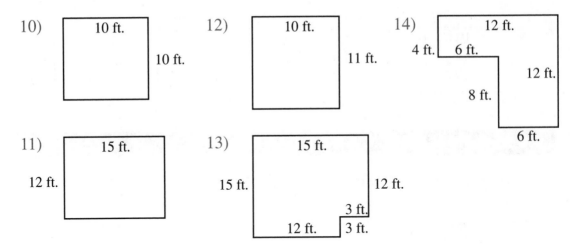

10) 10 ft. | 10 ft.

11) 15 ft. | 12 ft.

12) 10 ft. | 11 ft.

13) 15 ft. | 15 ft. | 12 ft. | 3 ft. | 3 ft. | 12 ft.

14) 12 ft. | 4 ft. | 6 ft. | 12 ft. | 8 ft. | 6 ft.

A *standard width* for carpet is twelve feet. You buy the number of feet of carpet you need from a big roll of carpet. It may make a difference in the amount of carpet needed if you use the twelve feet in the wrong direction.

EXERCISE B. Find the lowest price of a carpet for each floor. The laid carpet must be one complete piece. Some carpet will need to be trimmed.

Example: $11.45 per foot

$$\begin{array}{r} 11.45 \\ \times \quad 16 \\ \hline \$183.20 \end{array}$$

16 ft.

10 ft.

1) 12 ft. | 8 ft.

$11.45 per foot

3) 14 ft. | 12 ft.

$10.28 per foot

5) 13 ft. | 11 ft.

$7.89 per foot

2) 12 ft. | 10 ft.

$9.48 per foot

4) 16 ft. | 12 ft.

$8.98 per foot

6) 10 ft. | 11 ft.

$13.89 per foot

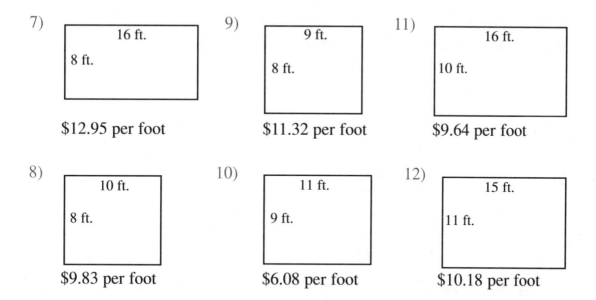

7) 16 ft. / 8 ft. — $12.95 per foot

9) 9 ft. / 8 ft. — $11.32 per foot

11) 16 ft. / 10 ft. — $9.64 per foot

8) 10 ft. / 8 ft. — $9.83 per foot

10) 11 ft. / 9 ft. — $6.08 per foot

12) 15 ft. / 11 ft. — $10.18 per foot

BUYING FLOOR TILES

Floor tiles are usually sold in cartons of 45. Each tile covers one square foot. You need to determine how many tiles you need by multiplying the length x width of the room. Divide that number by 45 to determine how many cartons you will need. Then multiply by the price to find your total cost.

Example: A carton costs $15.30. Each single tile costs $.35.

An 8-foot by 16-foot room
$8 \times 16 = 128$ tiles
$128 \div 45 = 2$ cartons and 38 single tiles
$\$15.30 \times 2 = \$30.60$
$\$.35 \times 38 = \$13.30$

	$30.60	2 cartons
+	$13.30	38 singles
	$43.90	Total cost

The cost is $43.90.

EXERCISE A. If a carton of tiles is sold for $15.30 and a single tile is sold for 35¢, find the cost of tiling each floor described below.

1) A 12-foot by 14-foot room
   ___ cartons
   ___ single tiles
   ___ cost

2) A 12-foot by 12-foot room
   ___ cartons
   ___ single tiles
   ___ cost

3) A room 9' by 14'
   ___ cartons
   ___ single tiles
   ___ cost

4) A room 8' by 12'
   ___ cartons
   ___ single tiles
   ___ cost

5) A room 7' by 9'
   ___ cartons
   ___ single tiles
   ___ cost

6) A room 10' by 12'
   ___ cartons
   ___ single tiles
   ___ cost

7) A room 8' by 11'
   ___ cartons
   ___ single tiles
   ___ cost

8) A room 8' by 14'
   ___ cartons
   ___ single tiles
   ___ cost

9) A room 10' by 10'
   ___ cartons
   ___ single tiles
   ___ cost

10) A room 10' by 15'
    ___ cartons
    ___ single tiles
    ___ cost

11) A room 10' by 16'
    ___ cartons
    ___ single tiles
    ___ cost

12) A room 13' by 15'
    ___ cartons
    ___ single tiles
    ___ cost

ESTIMATING THE AMOUNT OF WALLPAPER

Wallpaper is often sold by the *double roll*. You can estimate the amount of wallpaper that is needed to paper a room by using this rule of thumb:

• HOW TO MEASURE FOR WALLPAPER •

The distance around the room times the height of the wall divided by 60 determines the number of double rolls needed. Subtract one double roll for every four doors or windows. Always *round up* if you have a remainder after dividing by 60.

EXERCISE A.   Estimate the cost of wallpapering each of these rooms. The cost of one double roll is given.

Example:

One double roll of wallpaper costs $12.48.

12 feet		
9 feet	} Distance	42 feet
12 feet	around →	× 10 feet
+ 9 feet	room	420 feet
42 feet		

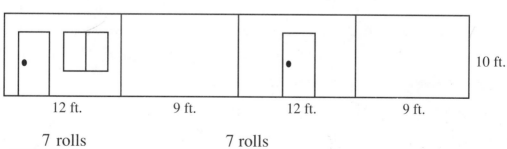

| 12 ft. | 9 ft. | 12 ft. | 9 ft. |

$$\begin{array}{r} 7 \text{ rolls} \\ 60\overline{)\,420} \\ 420 \end{array}$$

$$\begin{array}{r} 7 \text{ rolls} \\ -\ 1 \text{ roll} \quad \text{(For doors and windows)} \\ 6 \text{ rolls} \quad \text{needed} \end{array}$$

1) One double roll of wallpaper costs $11.98.

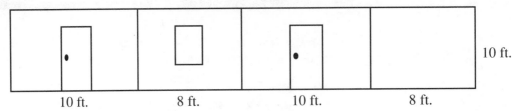

10 ft.

10 ft.   8 ft.   10 ft.   8 ft.

2) One double roll of wallpaper costs $9.95.

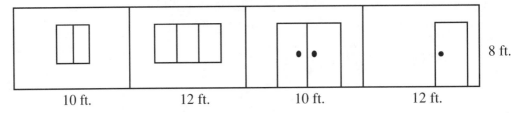

8 ft.

10 ft.   12 ft.   10 ft.   12 ft.

3) One double roll of wallpaper costs $15.45.

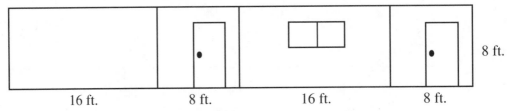

10 ft.

10 ft.   14 ft.   10 ft.   14 ft.

4) One double roll of wallpaper costs $13.28.

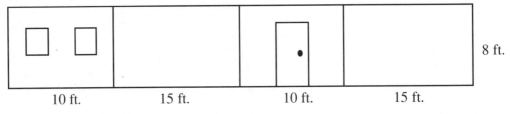

8 ft.

16 ft.   8 ft.   16 ft.   8 ft.

5) One double roll of wallpaper costs $17.49.

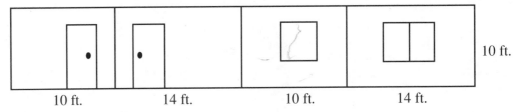

8 ft.

10 ft.   15 ft.   10 ft.   15 ft.

Calculator Practice 2

You can multiply quickly with a calculator. Key in each number. Verify it on the calculator display before you key in the sign or the next number.

CALCULATOR EXERCISE. Find the products.

1) 2706×412 4) 8017×217
2) 362×535 5) 6153×8715
3) 8711×305 6) 323×762

Computer Practice 2

Quotation marks are important in the BASIC language. Quotation marks tell the computer to print everything contained inside them exactly as it is typed. (See Appendix for more information.)

Example:

Multiply 235 and 62. Use this symbol (*) for multiplication.

Type on the computer:

PRINT   "235 * 62 = "; 235 * 62

Then press the RETURN or ENTER key. On the screen you will see the problem and the answer:

235 * 62 = 14570

COMPUTER EXERCISE. Use a computer to multiply the following numbers. Begin with PRINT and quotation marks.

1) 482×67 4) 2889×63
2) 534×29 5) 916×151
3) 371×296 6) 871×39

Find the answers.

1) 346
    × 7

2) 7) 5292

3) 408
    × 37

4) 14) 639

5) 60) 4740

6) 823
    × 226

7) 15) $34.95

8) $154.32
    ×   38

Find the surface area of the walls drawn below. Subtract the area of any doors or windows.

9)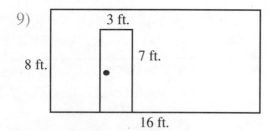

10)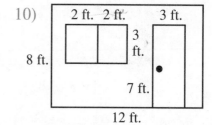

11)

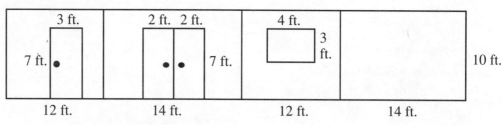

12) Find the number of double rolls of wallpaper needed to paper the room drawn in #11. Multiply the distance around the room by the wall height and divide by 60. Subtract one double roll for every four doors or windows.

Find the lowest cost of a carpet for each floor below if 12-foot wide carpeting costs $13.45 per foot.

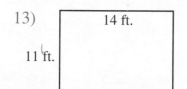

13) 14 ft. / 11 ft.

14) 10 ft. / 8 ft.

15) 12 ft. / 10 ft.

Find the number of square yards of carpet that are needed to carpet each floor drawn below.

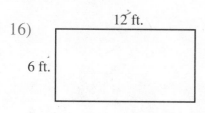

16) 12 ft. / 6 ft.

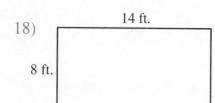

18) 14 ft. / 8 ft.

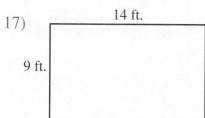

17) 14 ft. / 9 ft.

Find the lowest cost of tiling the floor of each room described below. Floor tiles that cover one square foot each are sold in cartons of 45 tiles for $17.00. Individual tiles cost $.38 each.

19)   A 12-foot by 15-foot room
___ cartons
___ single tiles
___ cost

20)   A 10-foot by 12-foot room
___ cartons
___ single tiles
___ cost

CHAPTER 3

INTRODUCTION

When you keep score in many sports, you add whole numbers. If your team scores a touchdown, you add six points to your *score*. In bowling you add seventeen points to your score when you get a *spare* followed by seven pins.

Many times you want to find the *average* of several scores. To do this you would add the scores and divide your answer by the number of scores. Before we begin using mathematics in sports, let's practice these skills.

EXERCISE A.   Find the sums.

1)
```
    15
    16
 + 17
```

2)
```
    12
     8
 +  4
```

3)
```
    18
    43
 + 26
```

4)
```
   123
   240
 + 178
```

5)
```
    36
    14
 + 12
_____
```

9)
```
    236
    248
 + 221
_____
```

6)
```
     7
    18
 + 26
_____
```

10)
```
    36
   129
 +  39
_____
```

7)
```
    14
     8
 + 21
_____
```

11)
```
   214
   196
 + 227
_____
```

8)
```
     8
     6
 + 52
_____
```

12)
```
   342
    96
 + 298
_____
```

EXERCISE B.   Find the quotients.

1) $6\overline{)438}$

2) $3\overline{)2937}$

3) $9\overline{)5373}$

4) $12\overline{)2796}$

BOWLING

Mathematics is used in scoring a bowling game. When you fill in a score sheet, you are adding the number of pins knocked down.

The large squares on a score sheet are called *frames*. A bowler may roll two balls for each frame. The number of pins you knock down with each roll is written in a small box in the frame.

Examples:

Karen played a 3-frame game. Look at her score sheet. Notice how the numbers are added.

1st frame: First roll   3
            Second roll   2

	1		2		3
3	2				
5					

2nd frame: First roll   4
            Second roll   5

	1		2		3
3	2	4	5		
5		**14**			

3rd frame: First roll   6
            Second roll   2

	1		2		3
3	2	4	5	6	2
5		**14**		**22**	

Total score: **22**

John bowled 3 frames with the following results.

1st frame: 1st roll   6
            2nd roll   2

2nd frame: 1st roll   5
            2nd roll   2

3rd frame: 1st roll   8
            2nd roll   0

	1		2		3
6	2	5	2	8	-
8		**15**		**23**	

Total score: **23**

When John hit no pins, a dash was written in the box.

EXERCISE A.   Write the number of pins knocked down in each frame below.

1)

1	2	3
3 3	6 3	2 6
6	15	23

3)

1	2	3
4 1	1 6	5 3
5	12	20

2)

1	2	3	4
2 5	4 2	5 -	5 4
7	13	18	27

4)

1	2	3	4	5
2 -	5 3	8 1	5 1	4 -
2	10	19	25	29

EXERCISE B.   Add to find the score for each frame below.

1)

1	2	3	4
2 3	3 4	5 3	8 -

4)

1	2	3	4	5
2 5	4 3	- 6	4 5	5 3

2)

1	2	3	4
4 3	1 7	2 6	5 1

5)

1	2	3	4	5
3 6	- 7	4 -	7 2	5 2

3)

1	2	3	4
6 2	4 5	7 2	- 3

6)

1	2	3	4	5
8 1	- -	4 5	2 1	6 3

EXERCISE C.   Construct a score sheet for each game below. Fill in the frames with the correct scores.

1)	1st frame:	1st roll	2
		2nd roll	3
	2nd frame:	1st roll	5
		2nd roll	4
	3rd frame:	1st roll	4
		2nd roll	5

5)	1st frame:	1st roll	1
		2nd roll	2
	2nd frame:	1st roll	1
		2nd roll	5
	3rd frame:	1st roll	3
		2nd roll	5

2)	1st frame:	1st roll	3
		2nd roll	5
	2nd frame:	1st roll	6
		2nd roll	2
	3rd frame:	1st roll	4
		2nd roll	3

6)	1st frame:	1st roll	1
		2nd roll	3
	2nd frame:	1st roll	1
		2nd roll	7
	3rd frame:	1st roll	3
		2nd roll	6

3)	1st frame:	1st roll	7
		2nd roll	2
	2nd frame:	1st roll	5
		2nd roll	4
	3rd frame:	1st roll	3
		2nd roll	5

7)	1st frame:	1st roll	2
		2nd roll	7
	2nd frame:	1st roll	3
		2nd roll	4
	3rd frame:	1st roll	8
		2nd roll	1

4)	1st frame:	1st roll	4
		2nd roll	5
	2nd frame:	1st roll	5
		2nd roll	2
	3rd frame:	1st roll	4
		2nd roll	2

8)	1st frame:	1st roll	3
		2nd roll	3
	2nd frame:	1st roll	5
		2nd roll	4
	3rd frame:	1st roll	1
		2nd roll	6

Scoring Spares. With a little luck you may topple all ten pins with two rolls of the ball. When you do this you score a spare. Getting a spare helps you to increase your score.

Example:

1st frame:	1st roll	3
	2nd roll	4

	1	2	3
	3 4		
	7		

2nd frame:	1st roll	8
	2nd roll	2

	1	2	3
	3 4	8 /	
	7		

The spare mark (/) means that 10 pins are scored in the frame PLUS the number of pins on the first roll of the next frame.

3rd frame:	1st roll	3
	2nd roll	6

	1	2	3
	3 4	8 /	3 6
	7	20	29

Explanation:

When a spare occurs in a frame, the total for that frame is the result of adding the previous frame total, plus 10, plus the number of toppled pins on the first roll of the next frame.

Example:

	1	2	3
	4 2	6 /	3 5
	6	19	27

1st frame:	1st roll	4
	2nd roll	2
2nd frame:	1st roll	6
	2nd roll	4
3rd frame:	1st roll	3
	2nd roll	5

EXERCISE D.   Write the number of pins that were knocked down on each roll.

1)

	1	2		3	
5	1	8		7	2
6		23		32	

6)

	1	2		3		4	
4	1	2		5	-	4	3
5		20		25		32	

2)

	1	2		3	
3	-	8		3	3
3		16		22	

7)

	1	2		3		4	
-	7	2	7	-	3	9	-
7		16		19		28	

3)

1		2		3	
4		5		5	2
15		30		37	

8)

1		2		3		4	
2		6	-	7	1	-	9
16		22		30		39	

4)

	1	2		3	3	2	4
8	1	7		5	3	2	4
9		24		32		38	

9)

1		2		3		4	
9		2		6	3	-	8
12		28		37		45	

5)

	1	2		3		4	5
6	2	6		8	-	7	4 5
2		10		19		25	29

10)

	1	2		3	5	4	2 3
3	2	6		5	4	2	3
5		20		29		34	

EXERCISE E. Construct a score sheet for each game below. Fill in the frames with the correct scores.

1)	1st frame:	1st roll	4
		2nd roll	6
	2nd frame:	1st roll	6
		2nd roll	3
	3rd frame:	1st roll	5
		2nd roll	2

2)	1st frame:	1st roll	3
		2nd roll	7
	2nd frame:	1st roll	5
		2nd roll	3
	3rd frame:	1st roll	4
		2nd roll	6
	4th frame:	1st roll	8
		2nd roll	0
	5th frame:	1st roll	5
		2nd roll	4

3)	1st frame:	1st roll	5
		2nd roll	2
	2nd frame:	1st roll	5
		2nd roll	5
	3rd frame:	1st roll	7
		2nd roll	2

4)	1st frame:	1st roll	5
		2nd roll	5
	2nd frame:	1st roll	4
		2nd roll	6
	3rd frame:	1st roll	1
		2nd roll	8
	4th frame:	1st roll	3
		2nd roll	4
	5th frame:	1st roll	3
		2nd roll	3

Scoring a Strike. A *strike* occurs when a bowler knocks down all 10 pins with the first roll of a frame.

The score for a strike is 10 plus the total number of pins the bowler knocks down with the next two rolls. A strike in the 10th frame gives the bowler two extra rolls.

Examples:

| | 1 | 2 | 3 |

1st frame: 1st roll   4

2nd roll   5

4 5

9

1   **2**   **3**

2nd frame: 1st roll   10

                2nd roll   —

4 | 5	⊠	
9		

3rd frame: 1st roll   7

                2nd roll   2

4 | 5	⊠	7 | 2
9	28	37

Fawn's score was 96 for the 6th frame. Her game continues as shown.

7th frame: 1st roll   10

                2nd roll   —

8th frame: 1st roll   3

                2nd roll   7

9th frame: 1st roll   6

                2nd roll   3

10th frame: 1st roll   10

                2nd roll   —

1st extra roll   10

2nd extra roll   9

6   **7**   **8**   **9**   **10**

5 | -	⊠ 3	◹ 6	3 ⊠	⊠ 9
96	116	132	141	170

EXERCISE F.   Fill in the frames with the correct scores.

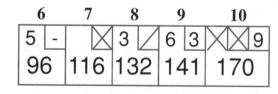

1) **1**   **2**   **3**

⊠ 9	- 7	1

2) **1**   **2**   **3**

⊠	⊠ 7	-

3) **1**   **2**   **3**

9 ◹	⊠ 8	1

EXERCISE G.   Construct a score sheet for each game below. Fill in the frames with the correct scores.

1)	1st frame:	1st roll	9	4)	1st frame:	1st roll	8
		2nd roll	1			2nd roll	2
	2nd frame:	1st roll	10		2nd frame:	1st roll	10
		2nd roll	—			2nd roll	—
	3rd frame:	1st roll	8		3rd frame:	1st roll	10
		2nd roll	1			2nd roll	—
	4th frame:	1st roll	5		4th frame:	1st roll	5
		2nd roll	2			2nd roll	0

2)	1st frame:	1st roll	5	5)	7th frame total:	85	
		2nd roll	3		8th frame:	1st roll	8
	2nd frame:	1st roll	10			2nd roll	2
		2nd roll	—		9th frame:	1st roll	10
	3rd frame:	1st roll	—			2nd roll	—
		2nd roll	10		10th frame:	1st roll	7
	4th frame:	1st roll	3			2nd roll	2
		2nd roll	2				

3)	1st frame:	1st roll	—	6)	7th frame total:	95	
		2nd roll	10		8th frame:	1st roll	8
	2nd frame:	1st roll	5			2nd roll	1
		2nd roll	4		9th frame:	1st roll	8
	3rd frame:	1st roll	10			2nd roll	2
		2nd roll	—		10th frame:	1st roll	10
	4th frame:	1st roll	8			2nd roll	—
		2nd roll	0				
					1st extra roll:	10	
					2nd extra roll:	9	

A Summary of Scoring. A complete game has ten frames.

Ordinary play: To determine a score for a frame, you add its pin count to the score of the previous frame.

Spare: After toppling all ten pins with two rolls, you take the previous frame total, plus 10, plus the number of pins on the first roll of the following frame.

Strike: After toppling all ten pins with the first roll, you take the previous frame total, plus 10, plus the number of pins knocked down on the next two rolls.

Example:

Mark bowled the following game. Study his score sheet for the correct scoring procedure.

1st frame:	1st roll	5		6th frame:	1st roll	3
	2nd roll	5			2nd roll	6
2nd frame:	1st roll	6		7th frame:	1st roll	10
	2nd roll	2			2nd roll	—
3rd frame:	1st roll	10		8th frame:	1st roll	0
	2nd roll	—			2nd roll	10
4th frame:	1st roll	9		9th frame:	1st roll	10
	2nd roll	1			2nd roll	—
5th frame:	1st roll	8		10th frame:	1st roll	10
	2nd roll	2			2nd roll	—
					1st extra roll	10
					2nd extra roll	9

1	2	3	4	5	6	7	8	9	10
5 ⁄	6 2	✕	9 ⁄	8 ⁄	3 6	✕	- ⁄	✕ ✕	✕ 9
16	24	44	62	75	84	104	124	154	183

EXERCISE H. Construct a score sheet for each game below. Fill in the frames with the correct scores.

1)

1	2	3	4	5	6	7	8	9	10
6 ⟨3⟩ 5	⟨2⟩ 8	1	⟨X⟩ 4	⟨5⟩ 9	-	4 ⟨5⟩ 3	⟨2⟩ 5	⟨4⟩ 4	⟨/⟩ 4

2)
1st frame:	1st roll	5
	2nd roll	4
2nd frame:	1st roll	6
	2nd roll	2
3rd frame:	1st roll	4
	2nd roll	6
4th frame:	1st roll	3
	2nd roll	5
5th frame:	1st roll	8
	2nd roll	1
6th frame:	1st roll	2
	2nd roll	8
7th frame:	1st roll	4
	2nd roll	5
8th frame:	1st roll	3
	2nd roll	7
9th frame:	1st roll	6
	2nd roll	1
10th frame:	1st roll	10
	2nd roll	—
	1st extra roll	9
	2nd extra roll	1

3)
1st frame:	1st roll	8
	2nd roll	2
2nd frame:	1st roll	6
	2nd roll	4
3rd frame:	1st roll	10
	2nd roll	—
4th frame:	1st roll	9
	2nd roll	1
5th frame:	1st roll	8
	2nd roll	1
6th frame:	1st roll	6
	2nd roll	3
7th frame:	1st roll	8
	2nd roll	0
8th frame:	1st roll	8
	2nd roll	2
9th frame:	1st roll	10
	2nd roll	—
10th frame:	1st roll	10
	2nd roll	—
	1st extra roll	10
	2nd extra roll	10

WEIGHTLIFTING

The sport of weightlifting will help to develop the body and to keep a person physically fit. Mathematics is needed in weightlifting to calculate weight totals. When you use mathematics in weightlifting, you need to know how to compute with zeros.

Examples:

Each member of the Martinsburg High weightlifting team lifted 200 pounds with barbells. If there were 23 members on the team, what was the total weight lifted for the team?

```
   200    Pounds each
×   23    Members
   600
   400
  4600    Total pounds
```

Kim Lee used two 10-pound dumbbells to help strengthen his upper arms. Kim's exercise schedule required 15 lifts with the dumbbells. What was the total weight lifted for each arm after 15 lifts?

```
    15    Lifts
×   10    Pounds per lift
   150    Total pounds
```

Marcell lifted 150 pounds on his first attempt. He increased the weight by 16 pounds on his second lift. What was the total weight he lifted on the second lift?

```
   150    Pounds
+   16    Pounds increased
   166    Total pounds
```

EXERCISE A. Practice your skill with zeros. Find the answer to each problem.

1)
$$\begin{array}{r} 200 \\ -\ 15 \\ \hline \end{array}$$

3)
$$\begin{array}{r} 670 \\ -568 \\ \hline \end{array}$$

5)
$$\begin{array}{r} 200 \\ -156 \\ \hline \end{array}$$

7)
$$\begin{array}{r} 200 \\ -198 \\ \hline \end{array}$$

2)
$$\begin{array}{r} 310 \\ -182 \\ \hline \end{array}$$

4)
$$\begin{array}{r} 320 \\ -196 \\ \hline \end{array}$$

6)
$$\begin{array}{r} 235 \\ -216 \\ \hline \end{array}$$

8)
$$\begin{array}{r} 230 \\ -\ 62 \\ \hline \end{array}$$

9) $310 + 296 + 400$

10) $506 + 23 + 915$

11) $7101 \div 9$

12) $4860 \div 12$

13) 320×50

14) $806 + 209 + 10$

15) $101 + 310 + 1091$

16) $3581 \div 10$

17) $2500 \div 25$

18) 4700×70

EXERCISE B. Solve these word problems.

1) Victor lifted a 95-pound barbell six times during his workout. What was the total weight that Victor lifted?

2) Donna lifted 55 pounds on her first attempt. She increased the weight by 20 pounds for the second lift. How many pounds did she lift on the second lift?

3) Melissa's weightlifting team lifted the following weights: 125, 90, 102, and 91 pounds. What was the total weight lifted by her team?

4) Jose's barbell set included a 45-pound handle, two 5-pound collars, two 10-pound plates, and two $2\frac{1}{2}$-pound plates. How much did the set weigh in all?

AVERAGES

When we compare performances in sports, we often use average scores. An average is found by adding all of the single scores and dividing the sum by the number of single scores.

For example, the Silver Stingrays, a bowling team, bowled 175, 182, 162, and 200. What was their average score?

Add.

$$\left.\begin{array}{r} 175 \\ 182 \\ 162 \\ +\ 200 \\ \hline 719 \end{array}\right\} \text{Scores}$$

Divide.

$$\begin{array}{r} 179\frac{3}{4} \\ 4\overline{)719} \\ \underline{4} \\ 31 \\ \underline{28} \\ 39 \\ \underline{36} \\ 3 \end{array}$$

The average score was $179\frac{3}{4}$.

Cory lifted 108, 105, 100, 99, and 103 pounds during the weightlifting finals. What was the average weight lifted by Cory?

Add.

$$\left.\begin{array}{r} 108 \\ 105 \\ 100 \\ 99 \\ +\ 103 \\ \hline 515 \end{array}\right\} \text{Weights}$$

Divide.

$$\begin{array}{r} 103 \\ 5\overline{)515} \\ \underline{50} \\ 15 \\ \underline{15} \end{array}$$

The average weight was 103 pounds.

EXERCISE A.   Find the average for each set of numbers. Write the remainders as fractions.

1)   26, 35, 20
2)   80, 83, 90
3)   180, 296, 121
4)   126, 103, 110
5)   165, 203, 175

6)   162, 200, 178
7)   202, 213, 185
8)   106, 115, 125, 163, 152, 128
9)   163, 200, 417, 831
10)   170, 117, 168, 200, 315

EXERCISE B. Find the averages.

1) The Lapton High School bowling team bowled 178, 186, 275, and 190. What was their average score?

2) Glenda's bowling scores were 263, 200, 217, 225, and 195. What was Glenda's average score?

3) For the first week of school, Anthony's calorie intake was 1951, 2065, 2419, 2315, and 2661. What was Anthony's average calorie intake?

4) Coach Thompson's weightlifting team turned in the following presses: 125, 105, 150, 95, 150, 145, and 72 pounds. What was the average press?

5) During the week of the New Castle bowling tournament, spectators numbered 175, 180, 165, 180, 170, 175, and 192. What was the average attendance for spectators?

Calculator Practice 3

Estimation. Before you use a calculator to find an average, estimate the sum of the numbers.

Example:

Find the average of 270, 420, and 305.

Step 1: Add. Estimate the sum first.

270	rounds to	300
420	rounds to	400
+ 305	rounds to	+ 300
		1000 Estimated sum

The exact sum on the calculator is 995. Since 995 is very close to the estimated sum, it is a reasonable answer.

Step 2: Divide. $995 \div 3 = 331.66666$

For this exercise we will use only whole numbers. The average of 270, 420, and 305 is 331.

CALCULATOR EXERCISE. Use your calculator to find the following averages. Estimate the sum of each set of numbers first. Use only rounded numbers to estimate.

	Numbers	Estimated Sum	Exact Sum	Average
1)	26, 28, 20	____	____	____
2)	38, 57, 31, 33	____	____	____
3)	58, 42, 48	____	____	____
4)	62, 69	____	____	____
5)	32, 36, 51, 20	____	____	____
6)	184, 108, 200, 190	____	____	____
7)	260, 221, 315	____	____	____
8)	3001, 2115, 2815	____	____	____

Computer Practice 3

To use the computer to find an average, you will use two important symbols in the BASIC language. Parentheses ( ) tell the computer what operation to perform first in an instruction. The slash / tells the computer to divide. (See Appendix for more information.)

Example: Find the average of 280, 420, 350. Type into the computer:
PRINT (280 + 420 + 350)/3

The computer will add the numbers inside the parentheses first. Then it will divide the sum of those numbers by 3. Press the RETURN or ENTER key for the answer, which is 350.

Instead of telling you to press the RETURN key, the symbol ® is used. When you are typing computer instructions from this book, press the RETURN or ENTER key each time you see ®.

Now type the same problem in a program format by numbering the instruction lines:
NEW
10 PRINT (280 + 420 + 350)/3 ®
20 END ®
RUN ® (This commands the computer to run the program.)

COMPUTER EXERCISE. Use the computer to find the average for each set of numbers. Use line numbers 10 and 20 for the instructions.

1)	263, 427, 295	3)	2963, 4834, 263, 915
2)	403, 209, 607, 493	4)	356, 291, 435, 262, 931

Construct a score sheet for each game. Fill in the frames correctly.

1)

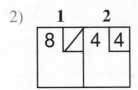

2)

1	2

3)

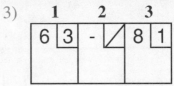

4)

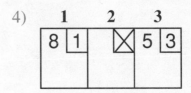

5)

1st frame:	1st roll	8	6th frame:	1st roll	6
	2nd roll	1		2nd roll	1
2nd frame:	1st roll	0	7th frame:	1st roll	1
	2nd roll	5		2nd roll	5
3rd frame:	1st roll	3	8th frame:	1st roll	7
	2nd roll	7		2nd roll	0
4th frame:	1st roll	6	9th frame:	1st roll	10
	2nd roll	4		2nd roll	—
5th frame:	1st roll	10	10th frame:	1st roll	6
	2nd roll	—		2nd roll	3

6) Marco increased his 123-pound bench press weight by 15 pounds. What was his new press weight?

Find the averages.

7) 39, 42, 65

8) 72, 83, 91, 39, 36

9) After a big calorie intake of 3145 calories, Kenny bowled 216, 195, and 190. What was his average game?

10) Jenny lifted these weights: 100, 80, 110, 140, 120, and 115 pounds. What was the average weight Jenny lifted?

CHAPTER 4

GAMES OF CHANCE

INTRODUCTION

Games usually involve some luck. You can play many games better if you know how lucky you need to be.

Mathematicians call the measure of this luck, *probability*. The probability that something will happen can be expressed as a ratio in fractional form. The closer to one whole this fraction is, the more likely you are to get the result you want. To do this you need to know how to *simplify* fractions to simplest form.

Example: Write a fraction to show what part is shaded.

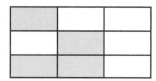

Step 1:   Use the total number of parts as the *denominator*. The total is 9.

Step 2:   Use the number of shaded parts as the *numerator*. That total is 4.

The total number of shaded parts is $\frac{4}{9}$.

EXERCISE A. Write a fraction to show what part of each figure is shaded.

1)

3)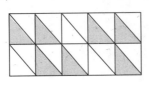

5)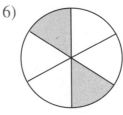

7)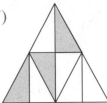

2)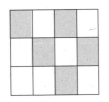

4)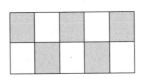

6)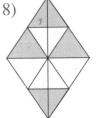

8)

EXERCISE B. Simplify each fraction to simplest form.

Example: Simplify $\dfrac{8}{12}$.

$$\frac{8}{12} = \frac{8}{12} \div \frac{4}{4} = \frac{2}{3}$$

1) $\dfrac{4}{6} =$

3) $\dfrac{12}{30} =$

5) $\dfrac{12}{52} =$

7) $\dfrac{13}{52} =$

2) $\dfrac{6}{12} =$

4) $\dfrac{6}{36} =$

6) $\dfrac{15}{36} =$

8) $\dfrac{24}{30} =$

Examples:
   Express $\dfrac{2}{3}$ with a denominator of 8.

$$\frac{3}{4} = \frac{?}{8}$$

Step 1: Divide the larger denominator by the smaller denominator.
   $8 \div 4 = 2$

Step 2: Multiply the quotient "2" by the existing numerator.
$3 \times 2 = 6$

$\dfrac{6}{8}$ is the new fraction.

Express $\dfrac{7}{8}$ with a denominator of 24.

$$\dfrac{7}{8} = \dfrac{?}{24}$$

Step 1: Divide the larger denominator by the smaller denominator.
$24 \div 8 = 3$

Step 2: Multiply the quotient "3" by the existing numerator.
$7 \times 3 = 21$

$\dfrac{21}{24}$ is the new fraction.

Express $\dfrac{5}{12}$ with a denominator of 24.

$$\dfrac{5}{12} = \dfrac{?}{24}$$

Step 1: Divide the larger denominator by the smaller denominator.
$24 \div 12 = 2$

Step 2: Multiply the quotient "2" by the existing numerator.
$5 \times 2 = 10$

$\dfrac{10}{24}$ is the new fraction.

EXERCISE C. Fill in the missing numerator by raising these fractions to higher terms.

1) $\dfrac{3}{4} = \dfrac{}{12}$

2) $\dfrac{5}{8} = \dfrac{}{24}$

3) $\dfrac{2}{3} = \dfrac{}{12}$

4) $\dfrac{1}{6} = \dfrac{}{24}$

5) $\dfrac{3}{8} = \dfrac{}{32}$

6) $\dfrac{4}{5} = \dfrac{}{10}$

7) $\dfrac{6}{7} = \dfrac{}{21}$

8) $\dfrac{5}{9} = \dfrac{}{36}$

FLIPPING COINS

When you flip a coin, there are two *possible outcomes*. The coin will either land on heads or tails. We can use a *probability tree* to help us keep track of several flips of a coin.

Example:

What are the possible outcomes of flipping a coin three times?

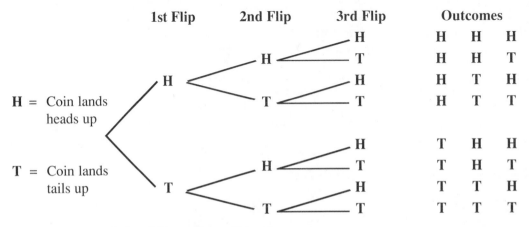

There are eight different possible outcomes.

EXERCISE A.   Use probability trees to answer the questions below.

1) How many different possible outcomes are there if you flip a coin two times?

2) If you flip a coin two times, how many outcomes give you a head and a tail?

3) Suppose you flip a coin four times. How many different possible outcomes are there?

4) How many outcomes give two heads and two tails?

5) How many outcomes give one head and three tails?

6) How many outcomes give four tails?

7) How many outcomes give three heads and one tail?

8) If you flip a coin five times, how many outcomes give three heads and two tails?

9) How many outcomes give one tail and four heads?

10) How many outcomes give no tails?

WHAT ARE THE CHANCES?

We use probability to measure how likely it is that an event will happen. We say that the probability of a event happening is the number of successful outcomes divided by the total number of possible outcomes. Probability is given in fractional form. In formula form this is:

$$\text{Probability} \quad = \quad \frac{\text{Number of successful outcomes}}{\text{Total number of possible outcomes}}$$

As an example, consider the *die* (singular form of *dice*). A die has six faces. Each face is equally likely to appear when you roll the die.

What is the probability that you will roll a 5?

We can use probability to predict how many times an event is likely to happen. For example, if Sam rolls a die 24 times, how many times can he expect to roll a 3?

The probability of rolling a 3 is $\frac{1}{6}$.

$$\frac{1}{6} \quad = \quad \frac{?}{24}$$

Sam can expect to roll a 3 four times out of 24 rolls.

EXERCISE A.   Answer these questions about rolling one die. How many times can you expect to roll...

1) a 5 out of 18 rolls?   6) a 6 out of 54 rolls?

2) a 3 out of 24 rolls?   7) a 4 out of 36 rolls?

3) a 3 out of 30 rolls?   8) a 2 out of 48 rolls?

4) a 7 out of 30 rolls?   9) a 2 out of 42 rolls?

5) a 1 out of 12 rolls?   10) a 1 out of 72 rolls?

PROBABILITY WHEN ROLLING DICE

When you roll two dice, the likely outcomes are not equal. This is because there are different numbers of *possibilities* of rolling each *dice sum*. You can roll a 5 by rolling 1 and 4, 2 and 3, 3 and 2, 4 and 1. You can roll a 4 by rolling 1 and 3, 2 and 2, and 3 and 1. You can roll a 5 four different ways, but you can roll a 4 only three different ways. Therefore, you will probably roll more 5s than 4s.

The chart on page 54 shows all of the possible outcomes of rolling two dice. The likely outcomes are equal in number.

EXERCISE A.   Answer these questions about rolling two dice.
1)   How many possible outcomes are there?
2)   How many different ways are there to roll a 6?
3)   What are all of the ways that you can roll a 6?
4)   What is the probability of rolling a 6?
5)   What are all of the possible ways to roll a 9?
6)   How many ways are there to roll a 9?
7)   What is the probability of rolling a 9?
8)   What is the least dice sum that you can roll with two dice?
9)   What is the greatest dice sum that you can roll?

EXERCISE B.   Fill in this chart about the probability of rolling a given dice sum.

Dice Sum	Probability of Rolling
2	_____
3	_____
4	_____
5	_____
6	_____
7	_____
8	_____
9	_____
10	_____
11	_____
12	_____

USING PROBABILITY

Many board games use the sum of two dice to determine how many spaces a player may advance on each turn. Below is the board for the game of *Journey*.

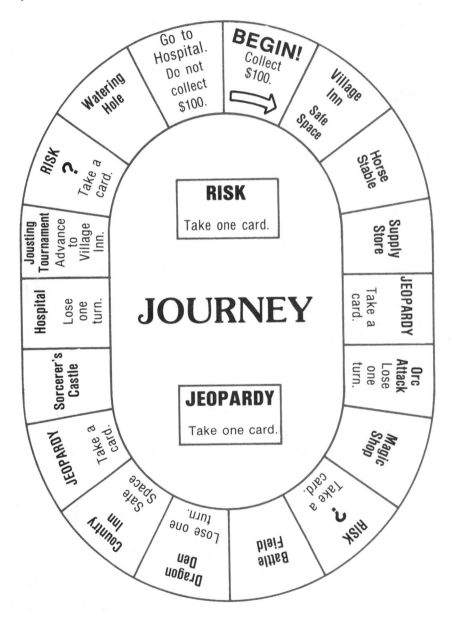

When it's your turn in the game of *Journey*, you roll two dice. Then you *advance* that number of spaces in a *clockwise* direction. You follow the directions printed in the space on which you land.

At each turn you are more likely to land on some spaces than on others. This is because there are more ways to roll the number which will place you on certain spaces.

For example, if you are on the BEGIN space, what is the probability that you will land on the Magic Shop on your next turn? This information will help you find a solution:

- Magic Shop is six spaces away.
- There are five different ways to roll a 6.
- There are thirty-six different outcomes of rolling two dice.
  Therefore, the probability of landing on the Magic Shop is $\frac{5}{36}$.

EXERCISE A.   Answer these questions about probability. You may need to simplify.

1) You are at BEGIN. What is the probability of landing on Orc Attack on your next turn?
2) You are at Battle Field. What is the probability of landing on Risk on your next turn?
3) What is the probability of landing on Supply Store from Village Inn?
4) What is the probability of landing on Country Inn from Magic Shop?
5) What is the probability of landing on Dragon Den from Village Inn?

More than one number on the dice roll might place you on the same square. For example, suppose that you are on Country Inn and you roll a 9. You would land on Village Inn. What would have happened if you had rolled a 4? You would have advanced to Jousting Tournament.

The directions there say, "Advance to Village Inn." The game has two events that would allow you to advance to Village Inn. Those events are: rolling a 4 or rolling a 9. In order to figure the probability of landing on Village Inn from Country Inn, we need to know the following:

Probability of Event A or Event B =
Probability of Event A + Probability of Event B

For example, what is the probability of landing on Village Inn from Country Inn?

This information will help you find a solution:

• Can land on Village Inn by rolling a 4 or a 9

• Probability of rolling a 4 is $\dfrac{3}{36}$

• Probability of rolling a 9 is $\dfrac{4}{36}$

• Probability of rolling a 4 or a 9 is $\dfrac{3}{36}$ + $\dfrac{4}{36}$, or $\dfrac{7}{36}$

Therefore, the probability of landing on Village Inn is $\dfrac{7}{36}$.

EXERCISE B.   Answer these questions about the probability of landing on a space from a given space. There may be more than one way of landing on the space, or there may be more than one of the spaces.
1)   From Horse Stable to Dragon Den
2)   From Dragon Den to Hospital
3)   From Orc Attack to Risk
4)   From Sorcerer's Castle to Village Inn
5)   From Orc Attack to Village Inn

EXPERIMENTAL PROBABILITY

When we roll two dice, we *expect* to roll a 7 six times out of thirty-six rolls, or one-sixth of the time. This is what we expect. This may or may not be what happens.

Let's try this experiment. Get two dice. Copy the chart on the next page. Each time that you roll the dice, make a mark on your chart next to the number that you rolled. Do this 36 times.

Number on Dice	Number of Times Rolled	Number of Times Expected
2		*1*
3		
4		
5		
6		
7		*6*
8		*5*
9		
10		
11		
12		

EXERCISE A.   Answer these questions about the chart that you have made.

1)   Was the number of times rolled the same as the number of times expected for any of the dice sums?

2)   Was the number of times rolled different from the number of times expected for any of the dice sums?

3)   Why do you suppose the number of times that you rolled some numbers was different from the number of times that you expected to roll those numbers?

MAKING PREDICTIONS

It is a little more difficult to determine how many times you can expect to roll a given number with two dice. This is because the probability of rolling each number is different for each dice sum. You can *predict* how many times you can expect to roll a given number if you remember the formula for finding probability:

Probability $=$ $\dfrac{\text{Number of successful outcomes}}{\text{Total number of possible outcomes}}$

Examples:

How many times can you expect to roll an 8 out of 72 rolls?

$$\frac{5}{36} = \frac{?}{72}$$

You can expect to roll ten 8s.

How many times can you expect to roll a 4 out of 60 rolls?

3 chances out of 36, or 1 chance out of 12 $\dfrac{1}{12} = \dfrac{?}{60}$

You can expect to roll five 4s.

EXERCISE A.   Answer these questions about rolling two dice. How many times can you expect to roll…

1) a 7 out of 24 rolls?
2) a 7 out of 18 rolls?
3) a 5 out of 36 rolls?
4) a 5 out of 18 rolls?
5) a 10 out of 60 rolls?
6) a 3 out of 54 rolls?
7) an 8 out of 108 rolls?
8) a 13 out of 24 rolls?

9) a 2 out of 36 rolls?
10) a 6 out of 36 rolls?
11) an 11 out of 54 rolls?
12) a 12 out of 72 rolls?
13) a 4 out of 72 rolls?
14) a 5 out of 63 rolls?
15) a 9 out of 27 rolls?
16) a 10 out of 48 rolls?

CARDS

A standard deck of playing cards has 52 cards in four suits: hearts, clubs, diamonds, and spades. There are 13 cards in each suit.

Given that information, what is the probability that if you draw one card, it will be a 7?

$$\text{Probability} = \frac{\text{Number of successful outcomes}}{\text{Total number of possible outcomes}}$$

$$\text{Probability} = \frac{4}{52} = \frac{1}{13}$$

There are four 7s out of 52 possible cards, so the probability of drawing a 7 is $\frac{4}{52} = \frac{1}{13}$.

Example:

What is the probability of drawing a red 10?

$$\text{Probability} = \frac{\text{Number of successful outcomes}}{\text{Total number of possible outcomes}}$$

$$\text{Probability} = \frac{2}{52} = \frac{1}{26}$$

There are only two red 10s, the 10 of hearts and the 10 of diamonds.

EXERCISE A. Answer these questions about the probability of drawing certain cards. What is the probability of drawing…

1) a jack?
2) a black 3?
3) a club?
4) a 5 of hearts?
5) a red 8?

6) a king or a queen?
7) a black card? 2 6
8) a face card (king, queen, jack)?
9) a 10 of spades?
10) a card less than a 7?
    (Do not include the aces.)

Rummy. In the game of Rummy, players are dealt seven cards. Then they draw cards and try to get three of a kind (such as three 7s) or a run in the same suit (such as the 3, 4, and 5 of spades). Because some of the 52 cards are already dealt, the probability of drawing a particular card is figured a little differently.

For example, study this seven-card hand:

What is the probability that this person will draw a 9?

52 cards − 7 = 45

Probability $= \dfrac{3}{45} = \dfrac{1}{15}$

(There are four 9s, but one is already in the person's hand.)

Example:

What is the probability that this person will draw a 3 of clubs?

Probability $= \dfrac{1}{45}$

(There is only one 3 of clubs.)

In both examples the total number of outcomes is 45 instead of 52 because seven cards are already in the hand (52 - 7 = 45).

EXERCISE B.   Answer these questions about the probability of drawing the card described. Remember to consider the cards that are already in the hand.

1)   What is the probability of drawing a jack?

3)   What is the probability of drawing the 6 of diamonds?

2)   What is the probability of drawing a 5?

4)   What is the probability of drawing a 2?

5) What is the probability of drawing a 4 or an 8?

8) What is the probability of drawing the 6 of hearts or a 3?

6) What is the probability of drawing a queen?

9) What is the probability of drawing a club?

7) What is the probability of drawing a 2, a 6, or a 7?

10) What is the probability of drawing a 3 or an ace?

Calculator Practice 4

Changing fractions to decimal equivalents can be easy on your calculator. Use the division function.

Example: Calculate $\frac{5}{7}$ as a decimal.

Solution: Press these buttons in order:

$$\boxed{5}\ \boxed{\div}\ \boxed{7}\ \boxed{=}$$

Answer: 0.7142857

CALCULATOR EXERCISE. Use your calculator to change each fraction to a decimal.

1) $\frac{5}{8}$ 5) $\frac{2}{9}$ 9) $\frac{10}{11}$ 13) $\frac{16}{17}$

2) $\frac{3}{7}$ 6) $\frac{1}{3}$ 10) $\frac{15}{17}$ 14) $\frac{28}{29}$

3) $\frac{1}{6}$ 7) $\frac{5}{6}$ 11) $\frac{20}{21}$ 15) $\frac{5}{13}$

4) $\frac{3}{4}$ 8) $\frac{4}{12}$ 12) $\frac{18}{19}$ 16) $\frac{3}{16}$

Computer Practice 4

Changing fractions to decimals can be easy when you use the computer as a calculator. (See Appendix for more information.)

Example: Compute the decimal of $\frac{5}{7}$.

Solution: Type on the computer: PRINT 5/7 ®
Answer on screen: .714285714

COMPUTER EXERCISE. Compute the decimal of each fraction below.

1) $\frac{1}{8}$ 4) $\frac{65}{77}$ 7) $\frac{1}{10}$ 10) $\frac{11}{15}$

2) $\frac{2}{11}$ 5) $\frac{15}{16}$ 8) $\frac{33}{34}$ 11) $\frac{23}{24}$

3) $\frac{1}{6}$ 6) $\frac{19}{20}$ 9) $\frac{11}{13}$ 12) $\frac{1}{19}$

CHAPTER TEST

Write your answers in simplest form.

1) $\dfrac{15}{36} =$　　　　　　　　　　　2) $\dfrac{39}{52} =$

Fill in the missing numerator.

3) $\dfrac{5}{6} = \dfrac{?}{42}$　　　　　　　　　4) $\dfrac{7}{36} = \dfrac{?}{72}$

When you are rolling one die, how many times…
5)　　can you expect to roll a 4 out of 18 rolls?
6)　　can you expect to roll a 2 out of 54 rolls?
7)　　can you expect to roll a 5 out of 42 rolls?

When you are rolling two dice, how many times…
8)　　can you expect to roll a 4 out of 24 rolls?
9)　　can you expect to roll a 9 out of 45 rolls?

What is the probability of…
10)　　rolling a 10?
11)　　rolling a 6?

This is part of a board game. Answer these questions about your next turn. For each question you start on the GO space.

GO ►	Horse Stable	Supply Store	Battle Field	DUNGEON Lose one turn.	Round Table Take a card.	RISK ? Take a card.	Plot against the King Go back 3 spaces.

For each turn you roll two dice, advance the number of spaces that you rolled, and follow the directions on the space that you land on. The cards that you draw give you special favors, but do not tell you to move to any other spaces.

What is the probability that…
12)   you will land on Battle Field?
13)   you will land on Risk?
14)   you will land on Dungeon?

A deck of 52 cards is shuffled. You draw one card.

What is the probability that…
15)   the card is a 6?
16)   the card is a club?
17)   the card is a king or a queen?
18)   the card is a 4 or a red 6?

Answer these questions about playing Rummy with a 52-card deck. Remember that seven cards are already in your hand.

19)   What is the probability of drawing a 6?

20)   What is the probability of drawing a 3?

CHAPTER 5

ADJUSTING RECIPES

INTRODUCTION

Preparing a fine dinner means following *recipes* and measuring ingredients. If the number of servings produced by your recipe does not match the number of people coming to dinner, you will need to adjust your recipe to suit your needs.

The mathematical skills needed to adjust recipes require the ability to multiply and divide with fractions and *mixed numbers*.

Multiplying Fractions — A Closer Look

Example: Find $\frac{12}{13}$ of $\frac{1}{4}$.   ("Of" means to multiply.)

Step 1:   Look for a common *factor* in the *numerators* and *denominators*. 12 and 4 have a common factor, 4.

Step 2:   Divide both the numerator and the denominator by the common factor.

$$\overset{3}{\cancel{\frac{12}{13}}} \times \frac{1}{\underset{1}{\cancel{4}}}$$

Step 3: Multiply the numerators.
Multiply the denominators.

$$\frac{3 \times 1}{13 \times 1} = \frac{3}{13}$$

EXERCISE A. Practice multiplying fractions. Write your answers in simplest form.

1) $\frac{2}{3}$ of $\frac{3}{4}$

13) $\frac{5}{56} \times 8$

2) $\frac{11}{12}$ of $\frac{6}{7}$

14) $12 \times \frac{8}{12}$

3) $\frac{22}{32}$ of $\frac{8}{11}$

15) $\frac{5}{11} \times \frac{2}{32}$

4) $\frac{5}{6}$ of $\frac{12}{25}$

16) $\frac{6}{9} \times \frac{9}{6}$

5) $\frac{17}{18}$ of $\frac{9}{10}$

17) $\frac{6}{7} \times \frac{7}{11}$

6) $\frac{10}{12}$ of $\frac{6}{10}$

18) $\frac{1}{8} \times \frac{18}{19}$

7) $\frac{5}{8} \times \frac{24}{25}$

19) $\frac{1}{4} \times \frac{4}{1}$

8) $\frac{13}{16} \times \frac{8}{9}$

20) $\frac{16}{19} \times 19$

9) $\frac{9}{20} \times 2$

21) $\frac{12}{13} \times \frac{13}{17}$

10) $\frac{7}{12} \times \frac{36}{42}$

22) $\frac{1}{6} \times \frac{3}{5}$

11) $\frac{28}{30} \times \frac{1}{2}$

23) $11 \times \frac{1}{11}$

12) $\frac{7}{33} \times 3$

24) $\frac{48}{64} \times \frac{16}{24}$

Renaming Mixed Numbers

Example:

Sandra has a great recipe for vanilla pudding that calls for $2\frac{1}{3}$ cups of milk. "$2\frac{1}{3}$" is a mixed number. Sandra must express $2\frac{1}{3}$ as an *improper fraction* before she can increase her recipe.

Step 1: Multiply the whole number by the denominator.

$$2\frac{1}{3}$$

Step 2: Add the numerator.

$$2 \times 3 + 1 = 7$$

Step 3: Write the answer over the denominator.

$$2\frac{1}{3} = \frac{7}{3}$$

EXERCISE B. Change these mixed numbers to improper fractions.

1) $2\frac{1}{2}$

2) $3\frac{2}{3}$

3) $4\frac{1}{4}$

4) $2\frac{2}{3}$

5) $3\frac{1}{5}$

6) $7\frac{5}{6}$

7) $4\frac{2}{5}$

8) $6\frac{1}{7}$

9) $11\frac{3}{4}$

10) $8\frac{3}{4}$

11) $7\frac{1}{7}$

12) $10\frac{2}{3}$

13) $5\frac{2}{5}$

14) $1\frac{1}{6}$

15) $3\frac{2}{5}$

16) $4\frac{7}{8}$

17) $1\frac{7}{18}$

18) $6\frac{9}{10}$

19) $10\frac{5}{6}$

20) $3\frac{7}{11}$

21) $13\frac{10}{12}$

22) $6\frac{1}{9}$

23) $7\frac{4}{5}$

24) $3\frac{7}{10}$

EQUIVALENT MEASUREMENTS

Ingredients in recipes are written many ways. It is helpful to know what the *equivalent* measurement is in case you need to adjust a recipe. Working with equivalents can simplify many recipe adjustments. The equivalents listed below should be a part of a cook's working knowledge.

2 tablespoons	=	1 ounce
3 teaspoons	=	1 tablespoon
16 tablespoons	=	1 cup
2 cups	=	1 pint
2 pints	=	1 quart
4 quarts	=	1 gallon

Examples:

4 tablespoons = ___?___ teaspoons

Rule: When you convert large units to small units, you multiply.
From the table, 3 teaspoons = 1 tablespoon.

$4 \times 3 = 12$ teaspoons

Solution: 4 tablespoons = 12 teaspoons

5 gallons = ___?___ quarts
From the table, 4 quarts = 1 gallon.

$5 \times 4 = 20$ quarts

Solution: 5 gallons = 20 quarts

6 pints = ___?___ quarts

Rule: When you convert small units to large units, you divide.
From the table, 2 pints = 1 quart.

$6 \div 2 = 3$

Solution: 6 pints = 3 quarts

EXERCISE A.   Convert the larger units to smaller units. Multiply to find the answers.

1)   3 ounces = ___ tablespoons

2)   2 tablespoons = ___ teaspoons

3)   2 cups = ___ tablespoons

4)   5 pints = ___ cups

5)   2 gallons = ___ quarts

6)   3 quarts = ___ pints

7)   7 ounces = ___ tablespoons

8)   3 cups = ___ tablespoons

9)   5 tablespoons = ___ teaspoons

10)   2 quarts = ___ pints

11)   56 ounces = ___ tablespoons

12)   15 tablespoons = ___ teaspoons

EXERCISE B.   Convert the smaller units to larger units. Divide to find the answers.

1)   8 tablespoons = ___ ounces

2)   6 teaspoons = ___ tablespoons

3)   64 tablespoons = ___ cups

4)   8 pints = ___ quarts

5)   16 quarts = ___ gallons

6)   20 quarts = ___ gallons

7)   6 tablespoons = ___ ounces

8)   10 tablespoons = ___ ounces

9)   12 teaspoons = ___ tablespoons

10)   8 cups = ___ pints

11)   36 tablespoons = ___ ounces

12)   16 pints = ___ quarts

INCREASING A RECIPE BY MULTIPLYING

To increase a recipe, multiply the amount of each ingredient by the same factor. All mixed numbers must be expressed as improper fractions before multiplying.

For example, Sandra's recipe for a frozen dessert will serve 8 people, but she wants to serve 16. What should she do?

Step 1:

$$\frac{16}{8} \quad \frac{\text{Amount to serve}}{\text{Amount in recipe}} = 2 \quad \text{Factor}$$

Step 2: Multiply each ingredient by the factor 2.

Frozen Smoothie (serves 8)	**New Amount**
$\frac{2}{3}$ cup chocolate syrup	$\frac{2}{3} \times \frac{2}{1} = \frac{4}{3}$
$\frac{2}{3}$ cups sweetened condensed milk	$\frac{2}{3} \times \frac{2}{1} = \frac{4}{3}$
2 cups whipping cream	$2 \times 2 = 4$
$\frac{1}{2}$ teaspoon vanilla	$\frac{1}{2} \times \frac{2}{1} = 1$
$\frac{1}{4}$ cup chopped nuts	$\frac{1}{4} \times \frac{2}{1} = \frac{2}{4}$

Now let's take a better look at the results of Sandra's multiplication.

New Adjusted Recipe
(serves 16)

$\dfrac{4}{3}$ cup chocolate syrup

$\dfrac{4}{3}$ cup sweetened condensed milk

4 cups whipping cream

1 teaspoon vanilla

$\dfrac{2}{4}$ cup chopped nuts

Renaming Improper Fractions. Sandra will have to simplify her fractions before she can begin to measure because some of the answers are improper fractions. They need to be *renamed*. To change an improper fraction to a *proper fraction*, divide the numerator by the denominator.

Example:
Change $\dfrac{4}{3}$ to a proper fraction.

Numerator: $\quad$ 4
Denominator: $\overline{\quad 3}$

$$3\overline{)4} \quad \begin{array}{c} 1 \\ \hline \end{array}$$

$$\begin{array}{r} 1 \\ 3\,\overline{)\,4} \\ \underline{3} \\ 1 \ \text{Remainder} \end{array} \qquad 1\,\dfrac{1}{3} \quad \begin{array}{l} \text{Remainder} \\ \text{Old denominator} \end{array}$$

Simplify Fractions to Simplest Form.   Think of the largest number that you can divide into both the numerator and the denominator with a zero remainder.

For example, to simplify $\dfrac{2}{4}$ to simplest form, the largest number that can be divided into both numbers is 2.

$$\frac{1}{2} = \frac{2 \div 2}{4 \div 2} = \frac{1}{2}$$

Example:
Increase this recipe to serve 24 people.

Potatoes Royal
(Serves 6)
6 baking potatoes

2 cups of boiled cabbage

$\dfrac{1}{4}$ cup melted butter

$\dfrac{1}{3}$ cup diced onions

Step 1:   Divide the new number of servings by the old number of servings to find the conversion factor.

$$\frac{\text{New servings}}{\text{Old servings}} = \frac{24}{6} = \frac{4}{1}$$

The factor is 4.

Step 2: Multiply each ingredient by the factor.

6 × 4 = 24 baking potatoes

2 × 4 = 8 cups of boiled cabbage

$\dfrac{1}{4}$ × 4 = 1 cup melted butter

$\dfrac{1}{3}$ × 4 = $\dfrac{4}{3}$ = $1\dfrac{1}{3}$ cups diced onions

EXERCISE A.   Increase these recipes to serve 12.

1) **Custard Ice Cream**
    (Serves 6)

$\dfrac{1}{4}$ cup sugar

2 tbsp. flour

$\dfrac{2}{3}$ tsp. salt

2 cups milk

2 beaten eggs

2 cups whipping cream

$\dfrac{1}{3}$ tbsp. vanilla

2) **Butterscotch Sauce**
    (Serves 4)

1 beaten egg yolk

$\dfrac{1}{4}$ cup butter

$\dfrac{1}{4}$ cup water

$\dfrac{2}{3}$ cup brown sugar

$\dfrac{1}{3}$ cup corn syrup

EXERCISE B.   Increase each recipe to serve the number of people shown.

1)   Increase to serve 24:
      Poppy-Seed Cake (Serves 8)

$\dfrac{1}{3}$ cup poppy seeds

$\dfrac{3}{4}$ cup milk

$\dfrac{3}{4}$ cup butter

$1\dfrac{1}{2}$ cups sugar

$1\dfrac{1}{2}$ tsp. vanilla

2 cups cake flour

$2\dfrac{1}{2}$ tsp. baking powder

$\dfrac{1}{4}$ tsp. salt

4 beaten egg whites

2)   Increase to serve 24:
      Hard Rolls (Serves 12)

1 package dry yeast

$1\dfrac{1}{4}$ cups water

$1\dfrac{1}{2}$ tsp. salt

$3\dfrac{3}{4}$ cups flour

1 beaten egg

3)   Increase to serve 27:
      Nut Loaf Bread (Serves 9)

3 cups flour

$\dfrac{3}{4}$ cup sugar

$3\dfrac{1}{2}$ tsp. baking powder

$1\dfrac{1}{2}$ tsp. salt

1 beaten egg

2 tbsp. melted butter

$1\dfrac{1}{2}$ cups milk

$\dfrac{3}{4}$ cup chopped nuts

2 tbsp. salad oil

4)   Increase to serve 30:
      Waffles Delight (Serves 10)

$2\dfrac{1}{4}$ cups flour

$3\dfrac{1}{2}$ tsp. baking powder

$\dfrac{3}{4}$ tsp. salt

$1\dfrac{1}{2}$ tbsp. sugar

2 beaten eggs

$2\dfrac{1}{4}$ cups milk

$\dfrac{3}{4}$ cup salad oil

DECREASING A RECIPE BY DIVIDING

A recipe may be decreased by dividing the amount of each ingredient by the same factor.

Example:

Sandra's recipe for vanilla pudding served 8 people. How can this recipe be adjusted so that it serves only 4 people?

Step 1: Divide the old number of servings by the new number to find the conversion factor.

$$\frac{\text{Old servings}}{\text{New servings}} = \frac{8}{4} = \frac{2}{1}$$

The factor is $\frac{2}{1}$.

Step 2: Divide each of the ingredients by the conversion factor.

$$3\frac{1}{3} \text{ cups milk}$$

$$3\frac{1}{3} \div \frac{2}{1} = \frac{10}{3} \div \frac{2}{1} = \frac{10}{3} \times \frac{1}{2} = \frac{10}{6} = 1\frac{2}{3}$$

$1\frac{2}{3}$ cups of milk are needed for the adjusted recipe to serve only 4 people.

EXERCISE A.   Practice dividing with mixed numbers.

1) $2\frac{1}{2} \div 4$

2) $3\frac{1}{2} \div 2$

3) $1\frac{1}{3} \div \frac{1}{2}$

4) $4\frac{1}{4} \div \frac{1}{2}$

5) $3\frac{2}{5} \div 5$

6) $2\frac{2}{3} \div \frac{1}{2}$

7) $4\frac{2}{3} \div 3$

8) $1\frac{1}{5} \div 1\frac{1}{2}$

9) $2\frac{3}{4} \div 2$

10) $5 \div 2\frac{1}{2}$

11) $1\frac{1}{6} \div \frac{2}{3}$

12) $2\frac{5}{6} \div 2\frac{1}{2}$

13) $3\frac{2}{5} \div 1\frac{1}{2}$

14) $1\frac{2}{3} \div 1\frac{1}{3}$

15) $5\frac{2}{5} \div 2\frac{1}{3}$

EXERCISE B.   Decrease these recipes to serve the number of people shown.

1) Decrease to 8:
Special Rolls (Makes 40)

5 pkgs. dry yeast

$3 \dfrac{3}{4}$ cups warm water

$12 \dfrac{1}{2}$ cups biscuit mix

5 tsp. poultry seasoning

$2 \dfrac{1}{2}$ tsp. celery seed

2) Decrease to serve 6:
Best Green Beans (Serves 24)

$1 \dfrac{1}{3}$ cups chopped onion

$5 \dfrac{1}{3}$ tbsp. salad oil

1 cup chili sauce

$1 \dfrac{1}{3}$ tsp. salt

8 cups green beans

3) Decrease to serve 8:
Super Meat Balls (Serves 32)
6 pounds ground beef
2 cups uncooked rice
4 tsp. salt
1 tsp. pepper
1 cup chopped onion
4 cans tomato soup
2 cups water

4) Decrease to 12:
Real Good Muffins (Makes 84)

$12 \dfrac{1}{4}$ cups sifted flour

14 tbsp. sugar

$17 \dfrac{1}{2}$ tsp. baking powder

$5 \dfrac{1}{4}$ tsp. salt

7 well-beaten eggs

$5 \dfrac{1}{4}$ cups milk

$2 \dfrac{1}{3}$ cups salad oil

5) Decrease to serve 8:
Nut-Orange Bread (Serves 56)

$15 \dfrac{3}{4}$ cups sifted flour

$5 \dfrac{1}{4}$ cups sugar

$15 \dfrac{3}{4}$ tsp. baking powder

$5 \dfrac{1}{4}$ tsp. salt

$1 \dfrac{3}{4}$ tsp. soda

$5 \dfrac{1}{4}$ cup chopped nuts

7 tbsp. grated orange peel
7 beaten eggs

$5 \dfrac{1}{4}$ cups orange juice

14 tbsp. salad oil

6) Decrease to serve 6:
Banana Bread (Serves 30)

$2\frac{1}{2}$ cups shortening

5 cups sugar

10 eggs

$3\frac{1}{3}$ cups mashed bananas

$6\frac{1}{4}$ cups sifted flour

$2\frac{1}{2}$ tsp. soda

$2\frac{1}{2}$ tsp. salt

5 tsp. baking powder

Calculator Practice 5

The calculator can help you compare fractions. First, calculate the decimal equivalent of each fraction. Then, inspect the two decimals and compare them. Finally, write the correct symbol (<, >, or =). Remember that "<" means "less than" and ">" means "greater than."

Example: Compare $\frac{5}{7}$ and $\frac{4}{11}$

$$\frac{5}{7} \quad ? \quad \frac{4}{11}$$

$$5 \div 7 \quad ? \quad 4 \div 11$$
$$0.7142857 \quad > \quad 0.3636363$$

$$\frac{5}{7} \quad > \quad \frac{4}{11}$$

CALCULATOR EXERCISE. Use a calculator to compare the fractions in each set. Use >, <, or = to compare.

1) $\dfrac{5}{6}$ and $\dfrac{4}{9}$

2) $\dfrac{7}{10}$ and $\dfrac{6}{11}$

3) $\dfrac{15}{17}$ and $\dfrac{18}{23}$

4) $\dfrac{13}{15}$ and $\dfrac{3}{4}$

5) $\dfrac{6}{13}$ and $\dfrac{7}{15}$

6) $\dfrac{8}{13}$ and $\dfrac{7}{12}$

7) $\dfrac{2}{35}$ and $\dfrac{5}{72}$

8) $\dfrac{15}{19}$ and $\dfrac{2}{3}$

9) $\dfrac{34}{35}$ and $\dfrac{61}{62}$

10) $\dfrac{4}{5}$ and $\dfrac{7}{9}$

11) $\dfrac{10}{11}$ and $\dfrac{11}{12}$

12) $\dfrac{6}{17}$ and $\dfrac{5}{18}$

13) $\dfrac{9}{10}$ and $\dfrac{11}{12}$

14) $\dfrac{10}{13}$ and $\dfrac{12}{17}$

15) $\dfrac{6}{13}$ and $\dfrac{7}{17}$

16) $\dfrac{13}{15}$ and $\dfrac{8}{9}$

17) $\dfrac{15}{22}$ and $\dfrac{14}{23}$

18) $\dfrac{9}{20}$ and $\dfrac{8}{21}$

19) $\dfrac{11}{35}$ and $\dfrac{21}{35}$

20) $\dfrac{1}{20}$ and $\dfrac{2}{31}$

Computer Practice 5

This program changes fractions to decimals. You can inspect the two decimals and see which is greater.
(See Appendix for more information.)

```
10    PRINT "CHANGING FRACTIONS TO DECIMALS FOR
            COMPARING"
20    PRINT "TYPE THE VALUES USING THE FORM A/B and C/D"
30    INPUT "A = ";A
40    INPUT "B = ";B
50    INPUT "C = ";C
60    INPUT "D = ";D
70    IF B * D = 0 THEN 100
80    PRINT "FIRST FRACTION = ";A/B
80    PRINT "SECOND FRACTION = ";C/D
100   END
```

COMPUTER EXERCISE.   Use the computer to compare the fractions in each set. Use >, <, or = to compare.

1) $\dfrac{23}{24}$ and $\dfrac{18}{19}$ 7) $\dfrac{53}{60}$ and $\dfrac{71}{80}$

2) $\dfrac{12}{22}$ and $\dfrac{4}{9}$ 8) $\dfrac{4}{11}$ and $\dfrac{5}{16}$

3) $\dfrac{17}{23}$ and $\dfrac{16}{25}$ 9) $\dfrac{2}{13}$ and $\dfrac{5}{16}$

4) $\dfrac{4}{7}$ and $\dfrac{15}{29}$ 10) $\dfrac{3}{25}$ and $\dfrac{4}{27}$

5) $\dfrac{8}{13}$ and $\dfrac{4}{5}$ 11) $\dfrac{10}{31}$ and $\dfrac{11}{32}$

6) $\dfrac{10}{11}$ and $\dfrac{20}{23}$ 12) $\dfrac{5}{16}$ and $\dfrac{3}{11}$

CHAPTER TEST

Find the answers.

1) After adjusting a recipe, Oliver needed $\frac{8}{24}$ cups of flour. What is the simplest form of the fraction $\frac{8}{24}$?

    a) $\frac{2}{6}$ b) $\frac{1}{8}$ c) $\frac{1}{3}$

2) Lynn's new cookie recipe calls for $2\frac{4}{12}$ cups of sugar. What is the simplest form of $2\frac{4}{12}$?

    a) $2\frac{1}{2}$ b) $2\frac{1}{3}$ c) $2\frac{1}{12}$

3) What is $\frac{2}{3}$ cup of chopped nuts multiplied by 6?

4) What is $\frac{1}{2}$ of $3\frac{1}{2}$ tablespoons of diced peppers?

    a) $3\frac{1}{4}$ tbsp.

    b)   7 tbsp.

    c) $1\frac{3}{4}$ tbsp.

5) Rename $\frac{5}{3}$ teaspoons of cream as a mixed number.

6) Rename $3\frac{4}{5}$ cups of all-purpose flour as an improper fraction.

7) How many ounces do 8 tablespoons equal?

8) How many gallons do 8 quarts equal?

9) Lauren and Bruce's bread recipe called for 6 cups of all-purpose sifted flour. How much flour will they use if they need only $\frac{2}{3}$ of the recipe?

10) Rick's cake recipe serves 6 people. It requires $2\frac{1}{4}$ cups of flour. How much flour will he need for a cake that serves 18?

CHAPTER 6

MATH AND CRAFTS

INTRODUCTION

When you do craft and sewing projects, you will be measuring with mixed numbers. For example, you might buy $4\frac{1}{2}$ yards of fabric and then need to measure $45\frac{3}{4}$ inches for curtains.

As you work with the fabric, you may need to add or subtract these measurements. You will be doing arithmetic with mixed numbers. Remember to write your answers in simplest form. Look at the examples below:

$4\frac{5}{8} + 2\frac{1}{8} = ?$

$$\begin{array}{r} 4\frac{5}{8} \\ + \ 2\frac{1}{8} \\ \hline 6\frac{6}{8} = 6\frac{3}{4} \end{array}$$

$2\frac{3}{8} + 4\frac{1}{4} = ?$

$$\begin{array}{rcr} 2\frac{3}{8} & = & 2\frac{3}{8} \\ + \ 4\frac{1}{4} & = & 4\frac{2}{8} \\ \hline & & 6\frac{5}{8} \end{array}$$

EXERCISE A.   Rewrite in vertical form and find the sums.

1) $6\dfrac{3}{5} + 7\dfrac{1}{5}$

2) $2\dfrac{1}{8} + 3\dfrac{3}{4}$

3) $1\dfrac{3}{8} + 7\dfrac{1}{4}$

4) $5\dfrac{1}{3} + 3\dfrac{1}{2}$

5) $7\dfrac{4}{9} + 2\dfrac{1}{3}$

6) $9\dfrac{1}{4} + 2\dfrac{1}{2}$

7) $3\dfrac{5}{12} + 4\dfrac{1}{6}$

8) $7\dfrac{1}{4} + 2\dfrac{1}{6}$

Some problems may result in improper fractions in the answer. Then you must change the fraction to a mixed number in simplest form.

Examples:

$$5\dfrac{7}{9} + 3\dfrac{4}{9} = ?$$

$$7\dfrac{5}{6} + 2\dfrac{1}{2} = ?$$

$$\begin{array}{r} 5\dfrac{7}{9} \\ + \ 3\dfrac{4}{9} \\ \hline 8\dfrac{11}{9} \end{array} = 9\dfrac{2}{9}$$

$$7\dfrac{5}{6} = 7\dfrac{5}{6}$$

$$+ \ 2\dfrac{1}{2} = 2\dfrac{3}{6}$$

$$9\dfrac{8}{6} = 10\dfrac{2}{6} = 10\dfrac{1}{3}$$

EXERCISE B.   Find the sums. Write your answer in simplest form.

1) $\quad 4\dfrac{5}{6}$

$\quad +\ 1\dfrac{1}{3}$

6) $\quad 14\dfrac{7}{8}$

$\quad +\ 6\dfrac{1}{8}$

11) $\quad 14\dfrac{5}{6}$

$\quad +\ 8\dfrac{2}{3}$

16) $\quad 16\dfrac{5}{6}$

$\quad +\ 17\dfrac{1}{2}$

2) $\quad 8\dfrac{1}{2}$

$\quad +\ 12\dfrac{3}{4}$

7) $\quad 9\dfrac{3}{5}$

$\quad +\ 4\dfrac{1}{2}$

12) $\quad 21\dfrac{7}{10}$

$\quad +\ 23\dfrac{9}{10}$

17) $\quad 46\dfrac{7}{10}$

$\quad +\ 29\dfrac{11}{15}$

3) $\quad 6\dfrac{5}{12}$

$\quad +\ 2\dfrac{1}{3}$

8) $\quad 5\dfrac{3}{4}$

$\quad +\ 7\dfrac{5}{6}$

13) $\quad 8\dfrac{5}{8}$

$\quad +\ 6\dfrac{2}{3}$

18) $\quad 32\dfrac{7}{8}$

$\quad +\ 59\dfrac{3}{4}$

4) $\quad 7\dfrac{3}{4}$

$\quad +\ 6\dfrac{2}{3}$

9) $\quad 5\dfrac{1}{2}$

$\quad +\ 4\dfrac{3}{4}$

14) $\quad 24\dfrac{3}{8}$

$\quad +\ 37\dfrac{1}{2}$

19) $\quad 64\dfrac{7}{12}$

$\quad +\ 89\dfrac{5}{6}$

5) $\quad 3\dfrac{3}{8}$

$\quad +\ 5\dfrac{1}{4}$

10) $\quad 7\dfrac{5}{8}$

$\quad +\ 1\dfrac{7}{8}$

15) $\quad 39\dfrac{5}{9}$

$\quad +\ 24\dfrac{2}{3}$

20) $\quad 38\dfrac{5}{6}$

$\quad +\ 56\dfrac{7}{8}$

WORKING WITH A FABRIC GUIDE

Many people sew their own clothes. Not only do they save money, but they can select the exact style and type of fabric they want.

When you buy a pattern, there is a *fabric guide* on the back of the pattern that tells you how much fabric you need. The amount of fabric depends on the width of the fabric.

Garment	Fabric Width	Misses' Sizes						
		10	12	14	16	18	20	
Top	36"	$1\frac{7}{8}$	$2\frac{1}{8}$	$2\frac{1}{8}$	$2\frac{1}{8}$	$2\frac{1}{8}$	$2\frac{1}{4}$	Yards
	45"	$1\frac{1}{4}$	$1\frac{3}{8}$	$1\frac{3}{8}$	$1\frac{5}{8}$	$1\frac{5}{8}$	$1\frac{3}{4}$	Yards
	60"	$1\frac{1}{8}$	$1\frac{1}{8}$	$1\frac{1}{8}$	$1\frac{1}{4}$	$1\frac{1}{4}$	$1\frac{1}{4}$	Yards
Skirt	36"	$1\frac{5}{8}$	$1\frac{3}{4}$	$1\frac{3}{4}$	$1\frac{3}{4}$	$1\frac{3}{4}$	$1\frac{3}{4}$	Yards
	45"	$1\frac{1}{8}$	$1\frac{3}{8}$	$1\frac{1}{2}$	$1\frac{3}{4}$	$1\frac{3}{4}$	$1\frac{3}{4}$	Yards
	60"	$\frac{7}{8}$	$\frac{7}{8}$	1	1	1	1	Yards
Pants	36"	$2\frac{1}{2}$	$2\frac{1}{2}$	$2\frac{5}{8}$	$2\frac{5}{8}$	$2\frac{5}{8}$	$2\frac{5}{8}$	Yards
	45"	$2\frac{1}{4}$	$2\frac{3}{8}$	$2\frac{5}{8}$	$2\frac{5}{8}$	$2\frac{5}{8}$	$2\frac{5}{8}$	Yards
	60"	$1\frac{3}{8}$	$1\frac{3}{8}$	$1\frac{1}{2}$	$1\frac{3}{4}$	$2\frac{1}{4}$	$2\frac{1}{4}$	Yards
Jacket	36"	$2\frac{3}{8}$	$2\frac{3}{8}$	$2\frac{1}{2}$	$2\frac{1}{2}$	$2\frac{5}{8}$	$2\frac{3}{4}$	Yards
	45"	$1\frac{7}{8}$	$1\frac{7}{8}$	$2\frac{1}{8}$	$2\frac{1}{8}$	$2\frac{1}{8}$	$2\frac{1}{4}$	Yards
	60"	$1\frac{1}{2}$	$1\frac{1}{2}$	$1\frac{1}{2}$	$1\frac{5}{8}$	$1\frac{5}{8}$	$1\frac{5}{8}$	Yards

EXERCISE A. Use the fabric guide to find the amount of fabric you need to make the garments listed on the next page. Be sure that you are using the correct fabric width.

Example:

How much 45" fabric is needed to make a size 12 top and a size 14 skirt?

$$1\frac{3}{8} = 1\frac{3}{8}$$

$$+\ 1\frac{1}{2} = 1\frac{4}{8}$$

$$2\frac{7}{8}$$

You need $2\frac{7}{8}$ yards of 45" fabric.

1) 45" fabric
   size 16 top
   size 16 skirt

2) 60" fabric
   size 18 jacket
   size 16 pants

3) 36" fabric
   size 20 top
   size 18 pants

4) 45" fabric
   size 14 pants
   size 12 jacket

5) 45" fabric
   size 18 top
   size 20 skirt
   size 18 jacket

6) 60" fabric
   size 14 top
   size 12 pants
   size 14 jacket

7) 60" fabric
   size 18 top
   size 18 jacket
   size 18 skirt

8) 45" fabric
   size 18 pants
   size 16 top
   size 16 jacket

9) 36" fabric
   size 16 top
   size 16 jacket
   size 18 pants
   size 18 skirt

10) 60" fabric
    size 12 top
    size 14 skirt
    size 12 jacket
    size 14 pants

11) 45" fabric
    size 12 top
    size 12 skirt
    size 12 jacket
    size 12 pants

12) 36" fabric
    size 14 pants
    size 16 top
    size 14 skirt
    size 16 jacket

MACRAME

Many people make decorative items by tying knots in *geometric* patterns. This is called *macrame*. Careful measuring is needed for a successful and attractive project.

EXERCISE A. Add to find the total length of each macrame project.

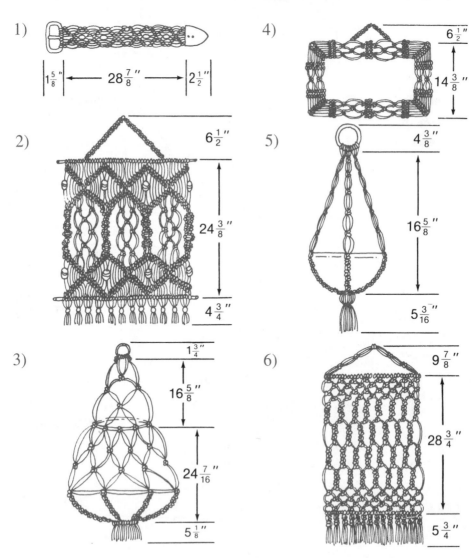

1)

$1\frac{5}{8}''$ ← $28\frac{7}{8}''$ → $2\frac{1}{2}''$

2)

$6\frac{1}{2}''$

$24\frac{3}{8}''$

$4\frac{3}{4}''$

3)

$1\frac{3}{4}''$

$16\frac{5}{8}''$

$24\frac{7}{16}''$

$5\frac{1}{8}''$

4)

$6\frac{1}{2}''$

$14\frac{3}{8}''$

5)

$4\frac{3}{8}''$

$16\frac{5}{8}''$

$5\frac{3}{16}''$

6)

$9\frac{7}{8}''$

$28\frac{3}{4}''$

$5\frac{3}{4}''$

You will need to subtract mixed numbers for some of your craft or sewing projects. In subtraction, just as in addition, you must have like denominators. *Examples:*

$$12 \frac{7}{8} - 3 \frac{5}{8} = ?$$

$$12 \frac{7}{8}$$
$$- \ 3 \frac{5}{8}$$
$$\overline{\hspace{2cm}}$$
$$9 \frac{2}{8} = 9 \frac{1}{4} \quad \text{Difference}$$

$$14 \frac{3}{4} - 6 \frac{2}{3} = ?$$

$$14 \frac{3}{4} = \quad 14 \frac{9}{12}$$
$$- \ 6 \frac{2}{3} = \ - \ 6 \frac{8}{12}$$
$$\overline{\hspace{2cm}}$$
$$8 \frac{1}{12} \quad \text{Difference}$$

EXERCISE B.   Rewrite each problem in vertical form and find the difference. Write your answers in simplest form.

1) $4 \frac{7}{8} - 1 \frac{3}{4}$

2) $6 \frac{2}{3} - 1 \frac{1}{4}$

3) $15 \frac{3}{8} - 7 \frac{1}{16}$

4) $15 \frac{15}{16} - 2 \frac{3}{8}$

5) $6 \frac{3}{4} - 2$

6) $17 \frac{7}{8} - 9 \frac{1}{2}$

7) $21 \frac{5}{6} - 13 \frac{3}{4}$

8) $4 \frac{3}{4} - \frac{5}{16}$

9) $12 \frac{7}{8} - 5 \frac{3}{8}$

10) $24 \frac{3}{8} - 17$

11) $15 \frac{4}{5} - 8 \frac{3}{10}$

12) $9 \frac{2}{3} - 6 \frac{1}{2}$

13) $29 \frac{5}{6} - 3 \frac{1}{3}$

14) $32 \frac{4}{5} - \frac{1}{2}$

15) $23 \frac{7}{8} - 16 \frac{1}{6}$

16) $23 \frac{7}{8} - 9 \frac{3}{4}$

17) $25 \frac{1}{2} - 18 \frac{1}{7}$

18) $45 \frac{3}{16} - 32 \frac{1}{8}$

19) $58 \frac{5}{8} - 6 \frac{1}{4}$

20) $9 \frac{13}{15} - 5 \frac{3}{10}$

After you have changed to common denominators, you may find that the top numerator is smaller than the bottom numerator. Then you must *regroup* before you subtract. Look at the examples below:

$$25\frac{3}{4} - 2\frac{7}{8} =$$

$$25\frac{3}{4} = 25\frac{6}{8} = 24\frac{14}{8}$$
$$- 2\frac{7}{8} = 2\frac{7}{8} = 2\frac{7}{8}$$
$$\overline{\qquad\qquad\qquad\quad 22\frac{7}{8}}$$

$$28 - 4\frac{3}{5} =$$

$$28 = 27\frac{5}{5}$$
$$- 4\frac{3}{5} = 4\frac{3}{5}$$
$$\overline{\qquad\qquad\quad 23\frac{2}{5}}$$

EXERCISE C. Find the differences. Write your answers in simplest form.

1) $13\frac{1}{8}$ $- 9\frac{1}{2}$

6) $42\frac{7}{16}$ $- 38\frac{5}{8}$

11) 48 $- 8\frac{7}{9}$

16) $29\frac{5}{8}$ $- 19\frac{5}{6}$

2) 15 $- 6\frac{7}{12}$

7) $21\frac{3}{4}$ $- 9\frac{5}{6}$

12) $33\frac{3}{5}$ $- 12\frac{1}{2}$

17) $9\frac{5}{12}$ $- 2\frac{3}{4}$

3) $28\frac{3}{4}$ $- 6\frac{5}{6}$

8) 42 $- 17\frac{5}{9}$

13) $26\frac{1}{8}$ $- 3\frac{3}{4}$

18) $29\frac{7}{8}$ $- 13\frac{5}{6}$

4) $17\frac{3}{8}$ $- 9\frac{3}{4}$

9) $32\frac{3}{4}$ $- 17\frac{5}{8}$

14) $15\frac{1}{3}$ $- 9\frac{1}{2}$

19) $42\frac{2}{3}$ $- 26\frac{7}{8}$

5) $17\frac{3}{5}$ $- 9$

10) $21\frac{1}{2}$ $- 17\frac{7}{8}$

15) 25 $- 14\frac{7}{12}$

20) $11\frac{3}{4}$ $- \frac{7}{8}$

SAVING SCRAPS

Whenever you work with fabric, you will have some scrap material left over. Careful placement of the pattern pieces may mean that the scraps will be large enough to use for some other project.

Example:

Find the length and width of the two rectangular pieces of scrap material, A and B.

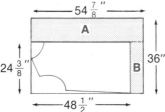

> Allow the length to be the longer measurement.

Piece A			**Piece B**		
36	=	$35\dfrac{8}{8}$	$54\dfrac{7}{8}$	=	$54\dfrac{7}{8}$
$-\ 24\dfrac{3}{8}$	=	$24\dfrac{3}{8}$	$-\ 48\dfrac{1}{2}$	=	$48\dfrac{4}{8}$
		$11\dfrac{5}{8}$			$6\dfrac{3}{8}$

Piece A	**Piece B**
Length = $54\dfrac{7}{8}$ "	Length = $24\dfrac{3}{8}$ "
Width = $11\dfrac{5}{8}$ "	Width = $6\dfrac{3}{8}$ "

EXERCISE A.   Find the length and width of the two rectangular pieces of scrap material in each of these ten patterns.

1)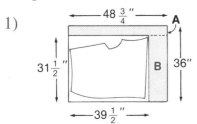

2)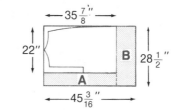

3)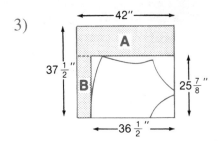

4)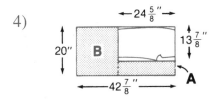

5)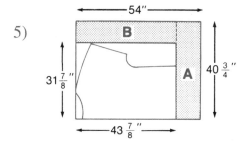

6)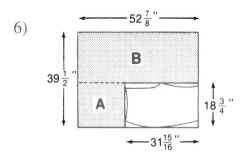

7)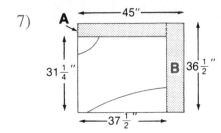

8)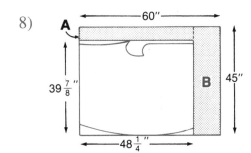

9)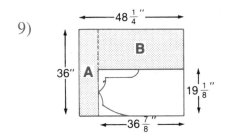

10)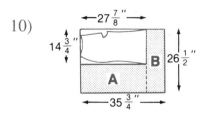

REPEATING PATTERNS

On some projects the same design unit is repeated over and over. This design unit is called a *repeat*. This repeat is the same length throughout the design. A repeat is measured from one design to the same position on the next design.

Example:

The pattern below repeats every $3\frac{1}{4}$ inches. How long will 20 repeats be?

$$3\frac{1}{4} \times 20 = \frac{13}{4} \times \frac{20}{1} = 65"$$

Twenty repeats will be 65 inches long.

EXERCISE A.   Answer the following questions about repeating patterns.

1)   A pattern repeats every $2\frac{3}{4}$ inches. How long will 16 repeats be?

2)   Another pattern repeats every $1\frac{7}{8}$ inches. How long will 20 repeats be?

3)   The belt is to have 18 repeats of $1\frac{3}{4}$ inches, plus $2\frac{3}{4}$ inches for a buckle. How long will the belt be?

4)   The repeat in a pattern is $2\frac{1}{4}$ inches long. How many repeats will there be in 36 inches?

5)   How many $1\frac{3}{8}$ -inch repeats will there be in $27\frac{1}{2}$ inches?

6)   This camera strap is to be 38 inches long. It will have 20 repeats of $1\frac{3}{4}$ inches each with equal borders at each end. How long will each border be?

7)   How long will 44 repeats be if each is $\frac{7}{8}$ inches long?

8)   How many $2\frac{3}{4}$ -inch repeats will there be in 33 inches?

Calculator Practice 6

Use your calculator to help you rename a mixed number as an improper fraction.

Example:

Rename $25\dfrac{3}{4}$ as an improper fraction.

Step 1: Multiply the whole number by the denominator.
$25 \times 4 = 100$

Step 2: Add the product to the numerator.
$100 + 3 = 103$

Step 3: Write the sum, 103, as the new numerator, and use the original denominator.

Solution: $25\dfrac{3}{4} = \dfrac{103}{4}$

CALCULATOR EXERCISE. Write these mixed numbers as improper fractions.

1) $12\dfrac{11}{25}$

2) $13\dfrac{5}{18}$

3) $16\dfrac{15}{16}$

4) $49\dfrac{12}{13}$

5) $9\dfrac{11}{34}$

6) $57\dfrac{5}{14}$

7) $24\dfrac{16}{17}$

8) $15\dfrac{23}{34}$

Computer Practice 6

Try this program to convert a mixed number to an improper fraction. (See Appendix for more information.)

```
10   PRINT  "CONVERTING  A  MIXED  NUMBER  TO  AN  IMPROPER
            FRACTION"
20   INPUT "WHOLE NUMBER = ";A
30   INPUT "NUMERATOR = ";B
40   INPUT "DENOMINATOR = ";C
50   PRINT "THE IMPROPER FRACTION IS ";A * C + B;"/";C
60   END
RUN
```

COMPUTER EXERCISE.   After you type RUN, answer the computer's questions. Use these mixed numbers for practice.

1) $26\dfrac{2}{3}$

2) $12\dfrac{13}{14}$

3) $18\dfrac{10}{11}$

4) $15\dfrac{16}{19}$

5) $28\dfrac{5}{11}$

6) $18\dfrac{12}{13}$

7) $29\dfrac{6}{7}$

8) $39\dfrac{10}{13}$

Find the answers in simplest form.

1) $6\frac{3}{4}$
$+\ 18\frac{1}{8}$

2) $9\frac{7}{8}$
$+\ 4\frac{1}{2}$

3) $12\frac{3}{4}$
$-\ 5\frac{1}{3}$

4) $17\frac{3}{4}$
$-\ 11\frac{7}{8}$

Use this fabric guide to answer the questions below.

Garment	Fabric Width	Misses' Sizes						
		10	12	14	16	18	20	
Top	36"	$1\frac{3}{4}$	$1\frac{7}{8}$	$1\frac{7}{8}$	$1\frac{7}{8}$	$2\frac{1}{8}$	$2\frac{1}{4}$	Yards
	45"	$1\frac{1}{4}$	$1\frac{3}{8}$	$1\frac{3}{8}$	$1\frac{5}{8}$	$1\frac{5}{8}$	$1\frac{3}{4}$	Yards
	60"	$1\frac{1}{8}$	$1\frac{1}{8}$	$1\frac{1}{8}$	$1\frac{1}{4}$	$1\frac{1}{4}$	$1\frac{1}{4}$	Yards
Skirt	36"	$1\frac{5}{8}$	$1\frac{3}{4}$	$1\frac{3}{4}$	$1\frac{3}{4}$	$1\frac{3}{4}$	$1\frac{3}{4}$	Yards
	45"	$1\frac{1}{8}$	$1\frac{3}{8}$	$1\frac{1}{2}$	$1\frac{3}{4}$	$1\frac{3}{4}$	$1\frac{3}{4}$	Yards
	60"	$\frac{7}{8}$	$\frac{7}{8}$	1	1	1	1	Yards

How many yards of fabric are needed for each project?

5) 45" fabric
size 14 top
size 14 skirt

6) 60" fabric
size 12 top
size 12 skirt

7) 36" fabric
size 10 top
size 12 skirt

8) 60" fabric
size 14 top
size 16 skirt

9) 36" fabric
size 10 top
size 10 skirt

Find the total length of each macrame project.

10) $1\frac{7}{8}''$ $\longleftarrow$ $29\frac{3}{4}''$ $\longrightarrow$ $2\frac{3}{8}''$

11)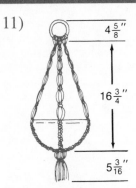

Find the length and width of these pieces of scrap material, A and B.

12)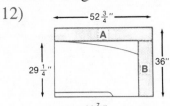

13)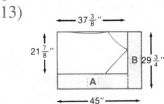

Answer these questions about repeating patterns.

14) Anna Wilson is making a border that has a repeating pattern. The pattern repeats every $1\frac{3}{4}$ inches. How long will 14 repeats be?

15) Carla Weaver's belt is to have 15 repeats of $1\frac{7}{8}$ inches plus $3\frac{5}{8}$ inches for the buckle. How long will the finished belt be?

16) Diane Mason is making a camera strap which is to be 38 inches long. It will have 12 repeats of $2\frac{3}{4}$ inches each with equal borders at each end. How long will each of the two borders be?

17) How long will 23 repeats be if each is $3\frac{1}{8}$ inches long?

Find the missing numerators.

18) $14\frac{5}{8} = 13\frac{?}{8}$

19) $8 = 7\frac{?}{3}$

20) $25\frac{3}{4} = 24\frac{?}{8}$

CHAPTER 7

FRACTIONS IN THE HOME

INTRODUCTION

We will use fractions in many of our projects around the house. If you make book shelves that are each $34\frac{3}{4}$ inches long, you would multiply by the number of shelves to find the length of board you will need to buy. You would divide fractions to find the number of ribbons each $8\frac{1}{2}$ inches long you can cut from a longer piece of ribbon.

To find the amount of flour you would need to make a cake, a pie, and two batches of cookies, you would add fractions. You would subtract fractions to find out how much fabric would be left after making a new outfit. Knowing how to do arithmetic with fractions will help you in your home projects.

ADDITION OF FRACTIONS

When you are finding the total measurement of two or more items, you may have to add fractions. Be careful to keep the same unit of measure within the same problem.

For example, Lisa wants to combine $2\frac{3}{4}$ cups of flour and one pint of milk. How many cups in all does that make? Remember, one pint equals two cups.

$$2\frac{3}{4} \text{ cups of flour} \qquad = 2\frac{3}{4} \text{ cups of flour}$$

$$+ \quad 1 \qquad \text{pint of milk} \qquad = 2 \qquad \text{cups of milk}$$

$$4\frac{3}{4} \text{ cups}$$

Answer: $4\frac{3}{4}$ cups in all

Lori bought $2\frac{1}{2}$ yards of green material and $3\frac{2}{3}$ yards of red. How many yards of material did Lori buy?

$$2\frac{1}{2} = 2\frac{3}{6}$$

$$+ \quad 3\frac{2}{3} = 3\frac{4}{6}$$

$$5\frac{7}{6} = 6\frac{1}{6}$$

Answer: $6\frac{1}{6}$ yards

Remember:
$$5\frac{7}{6} = 5 + \frac{7}{6}$$
$$= 5 + 1\frac{1}{6}$$
$$= 6\frac{1}{6}$$

EXERCISE A. Practice adding fractions. Write your answers in simplest form.

1) $2\dfrac{3}{4}$
   $+\ 1\dfrac{1}{5}$

3) $4\dfrac{3}{7}$
   $+\ 2\dfrac{5}{6}$

5) 12
   $+\ 2\dfrac{5}{6}$

7) 5
   $+\ 3\dfrac{7}{8}$

2) $5\dfrac{2}{5}$
   $+\ 1\dfrac{4}{6}$

4) 2
   $+\ 9\dfrac{1}{8}$

6) 8
   $+\ 3\dfrac{1}{4}$

8) $3\dfrac{1}{8}$
   $+\ 5\dfrac{1}{6}$

EXERCISE B. Solve these problems. Write your answers in the correct units of measure.

1) $2\dfrac{1}{3}$ yards $+ 1\dfrac{1}{2}$ ft.

2) $2\dfrac{1}{2}$ pints $+ 3\dfrac{3}{4}$ cups

3) Carlos bought $6\dfrac{1}{2}$ feet of blue webbing and $3\dfrac{4}{5}$ feet of yellow webbing to fix his lawn chairs. What was the total number of feet bought?

4) Jacob measured the distance around his patio and made the following measurements: $12\dfrac{1}{4}$ feet, $16\dfrac{2}{3}$ feet, $12\dfrac{1}{4}$ feet, and $16\dfrac{2}{3}$ feet. Find the perimeter of the patio. (The perimeter equals the sum of the sides.)

5) Victor was asked to bake two cakes and one batch of cookies for the school bake sale. His flour needs are $2\dfrac{1}{2}$ cups, 3 cups, and $2\dfrac{1}{3}$ cups. Find the total number of cups needed.

6) Tess's economical notebook paper measures $7\dfrac{15}{16}$ inches for the width and $10\dfrac{7}{8}$ inches for the length. Find the perimeter of Tess's notebook paper.

SUBTRACTION OF FRACTIONS

When you measure items, you may need to subtract quantities with fractions.

Examples:

Maria bought a quart of mayonnaise. She used $2\frac{1}{3}$ cups in a large salad. How many cups of mayonnaise were left? (One quart = 4 cups)

$$4 \quad \text{cups} \; = \; 3\frac{3}{3} \; \text{cups}$$
$$- \; 2\frac{1}{3} \; \text{cups} \; = \; 2\frac{1}{3} \; \text{cups}$$
$$1\frac{2}{3} \; \text{cups}$$

$$4 \; = \; 3 + 1$$
$$= \; 3 + \frac{3}{3}$$
$$= \; 3\frac{3}{3}$$

Answer: $1\frac{2}{3}$ cups of mayonnaise were left.

Warren used $6\frac{3}{4}$ feet of a $12\frac{1}{8}$-foot board. How much of the board was left?

$$12\frac{1}{8} \; = \; 12\frac{1}{8} \; = \; 11\frac{9}{8}$$
$$- \; 6\frac{3}{4} \; = \; 6\frac{6}{8} \; = \; 6\frac{6}{8}$$
$$5\frac{3}{8}$$

Answer: $5\frac{3}{8}$ feet were left.

$$12\frac{1}{8} \; = \; 11 + 1 + \frac{1}{8}$$
$$= \; 11 + \frac{8}{8} + \frac{1}{8}$$
$$= \; 11 + \frac{9}{8}$$
$$= \; 11\frac{9}{8}$$

EXERCISE A. Practice subtracting fractions. Write your answers in simplest form.

1)   13

   $- 5\dfrac{2}{3}$
   _____

2) $6\dfrac{5}{8}$

   $- 2\dfrac{1}{3}$
   _____

3) $3\dfrac{1}{6}$

   $- 2\dfrac{3}{8}$
   _____

4) $18\dfrac{5}{6}$

   $- 2\dfrac{4}{11}$
   _____

5) $4\dfrac{6}{11}$

   $- \dfrac{3}{4}$
   _____

6)   15

   $- 2\dfrac{1}{10}$
   _____

7) $5\dfrac{2}{3}$

   $- \dfrac{8}{9}$
   _____

8) $13\dfrac{2}{7}$

   $- 3\dfrac{13}{14}$
   _____

EXERCISE B. Solve these problems. Write your answers in the correct units.

1) 1 yard - $16\dfrac{1}{4}$ inches

2) 2 quarts - $5\dfrac{1}{2}$ cups

3) Sid used $2\dfrac{5}{8}$ yards of a 6-yard piece of canvas to patch his tent. How many yards were left?

4) Lelia needed a shade for a window that was $48\dfrac{3}{4}$ inches long. She found a shade that was 72" long. How much longer was the shade than the window?

5) Mike had $6\dfrac{3}{4}$ gallons of white paint and 7 quarts of green paint. How much more white paint than green paint did he have?

6) Russ bought 6 feet of picture wire. He used $29\dfrac{1}{2}$ inches to hang a mirror. How much did he have left?

CHAPTER 7

MULTIPLICATION OF FRACTIONS

Frequently home projects involve using measurements. If one measurement is repeated many times, you must multiply to find the total length.

Example:

Mark wants to make a bookcase with four shelves to fit between two windows. Each shelf is to be $23\frac{1}{2}$ inches long. How many inches of shelving will he need?

To find the total length of shelving needed, he would have to multiply $23\frac{1}{2}$" times 4.

$$23\frac{1}{2} \times 4 =$$

Write mixed numbers as improper fractions.

$$\frac{47}{\underset{1}{\cancel{2}}} \times \frac{\cancel{4}^{\,2}}{1} =$$

$$\frac{47}{1} \times \frac{2}{1} = \frac{94}{1} = 94 \text{ inches of shelving}$$

EXERCISE A.   Find the inches of shelving needed for each project.

1) $16\frac{1}{4}$" $\times$ 7

2) $13\frac{3}{4}$" $\times$ 4

3) $24\frac{7}{8}$" $\times$ 6

4) $28\frac{1}{4}$" $\times$ 16

5) $38\frac{1}{8}$" $\times$ 10

6) $60\frac{1}{4}$" $\times$ 10

7) $13\frac{1}{2}$" $\times$ 5

8) $16\frac{7}{8}$" $\times$ 3

9) $30\frac{4}{5}$" $\times$ 2

10) $6\frac{1}{8}$" $\times$ 22

11) $5\frac{3}{4}$" $\times$ 20

12) $9\frac{2}{7}$" $\times$ 16

Finding the Area. To find the *area* of a surface, you multiply. For example, Charlie's hobby is gardening. He is getting ready to plant flowers in a large, raised flower bed. The bed is $13\frac{1}{2}$ feet long, and $12\frac{3}{4}$ feet wide. What is the area? Remember, the area equals the length times the width.

$$\text{Length} \times \text{Width} = \text{Area}$$

$$13\frac{1}{2} \times 12\frac{3}{4} =$$

$$\frac{27}{2} \times \frac{51}{4} = \frac{1377}{8} = 172\frac{1}{8} \text{ square feet}$$

Write your answer in square feet.

EXERCISE B.   Find the area of each surface. Write your answer in square units.

1) $2\frac{1}{3}$ feet $\times$ 3 ft.

2) $2\frac{3}{5}$ inches $\times$ 20 in.

3) $\frac{4}{7}$ meters $\times$ 5 m

4) $4\frac{2}{3}$ cm $\times$ 30 cm

5) $1\frac{1}{2}$ mm $\times$ $2\frac{5}{6}$ mm

6) 3 cm $\times$ $\frac{3}{4}$ cm

7) $5\frac{3}{8}$ in. $\times$ $5\frac{2}{3}$ in.

8) $3\frac{7}{8}$ m $\times$ $\frac{4}{5}$ m

9) 8 yds. $\times$ $16\frac{2}{9}$ yds.

10) $6\frac{3}{4}$ mm $\times$ 12 mm

11) 14 in. $\times$ $5\frac{4}{7}$ in.

12) $13\frac{4}{9}$ yd. $\times$ $\frac{5}{8}$ yd.

13) $9\frac{1}{2}$ cm $\times$ 6 cm

14) $8\frac{1}{3}$ mm $\times$ $2\frac{1}{2}$ mm

EXERCISE C.   Practice multiplying with fractions.   Find these lengths. Write your answers in the units given.

1) $3\frac{1}{2}$ ft. $\times$ 3

2) $6\frac{2}{3}$ in. $\times \frac{1}{2}$

3) $2\frac{3}{4}$ m $\times$ 5

4) $1\frac{1}{5}$ yd. $\times$ 5

5) $1\frac{2}{5}$ in. $\times 1\frac{1}{2}$

6) $5\frac{2}{5}$ ft. $\times 1\frac{1}{3}$

7)   21 mm $\times \frac{2}{3}$

8) $3\frac{2}{9}$ mm $\times 2\frac{1}{12}$

9) $1\frac{1}{3}$ ft. $\times 1\frac{1}{5}$

10) $2\frac{1}{6}$ yd. $\times 1\frac{1}{6}$

11) $2\frac{3}{4}$ mm $\times 1\frac{1}{2}$

12) $7\frac{2}{5}$ ft. $\times 2\frac{2}{3}$

EXERCISE D.   Solve these problems.   Write your answers in the correct units of measure.

1)   Diana's gravy recipe calls for $2\frac{1}{2}$ tablespoons of cornstarch. How much will she need if she makes only $\frac{2}{3}$ of the recipe?

2)   Hugh's bookshelf plan calls for 5 shelves, each measuring $25\frac{1}{2}$ inches. Find the total length of shelving in inches.

3)   Elliott is installing wall-to-wall carpeting in his den. If the room measures 13 by $14\frac{1}{2}$ feet, how many square feet of carpeting will he need?

4)   Deborah's kitchen measures 16 by $12\frac{1}{4}$ feet. If she is installing one-square-foot tiles, how many tiles will she need?

5)   Brian purchased $20\frac{1}{2}$ feet of hall carpet and had $\frac{2}{3}$ of this left. How many feet did he have left?

DIVISION OF MIXED NUMBERS & FRACTIONS

To divide a mixed number, first change the mixed number to a fraction. Then *invert* the divisor and multiply. For example, if Eve bought $25\frac{1}{3}$ feet of shelf paper. How many 5-foot shelves can be covered with this? Eve should use division to solve this problem.

$$25\frac{1}{3} \div 5 =$$

$$\frac{76}{3} \div \frac{5}{1} =$$

$$\frac{76}{3} \times \frac{1}{5} = \frac{76}{15} = 5\frac{1}{15}$$

Five shelves can be covered. The remainder of $\frac{1}{15}$ is not enough to cover a complete shelf.

Example:

Tony's apartment has a balcony that is $2\frac{1}{3}$ yards wide. Its area is $9\frac{1}{3}$ square yards. What is the length of the balcony?

Area $\div$ Width $=$ Length

$$9\frac{1}{3} \div 2\frac{1}{3} =$$

$$\frac{28}{3} \div \frac{7}{3} =$$

$$\overset{4}{\underset{1}{\frac{\cancel{28}}{\cancel{3}}}} \times \overset{1}{\underset{1}{\frac{\cancel{3}}{\cancel{7}}}} = \frac{4}{1} = 4 \text{ yards}$$

The balcony is 4 yards long.

EXERCISE A.   Practice dividing with fractions and mixed numbers.

1) $\dfrac{5}{6} \div \dfrac{2}{3}$

2) $\dfrac{4}{5} \div 8$

3) $2\dfrac{3}{4} \div \dfrac{6}{7}$

4) $5\dfrac{1}{7} \div \dfrac{2}{5}$

5) $6\dfrac{2}{5} \div 1\dfrac{1}{2}$

6) $5\dfrac{2}{3} \div 2\dfrac{1}{2}$

7) $4\dfrac{1}{3} \div 12$

8) $6\dfrac{2}{9} \div 3$

9) $5\dfrac{2}{8} \div \dfrac{5}{6}$

10) $7\dfrac{1}{7} \div 10$

11) $5 \div \dfrac{2}{5}$

12) $3\dfrac{4}{5} \div 3\dfrac{1}{8}$

13) $4\dfrac{1}{3} \div 1\dfrac{1}{2}$

14) $6 \div 2\dfrac{6}{7}$

15) $6\dfrac{2}{5} \div 1\dfrac{1}{5}$

16) $2\dfrac{7}{8} \div 1\dfrac{1}{4}$

EXERCISE B.   Solve these problems. Write your answers in the correct units.

1) If the area of a cabinet top is $3\dfrac{1}{2}$ square meters, and the length is $1\dfrac{1}{4}$ meters, what is the width?

2) Jeff's recipe for barbecue sauce calls for $2\dfrac{1}{3}$ tablespoons of vinegar. How much vinegar will he use if he divides the recipe by 4?

3) Ted's project calls for $15\dfrac{1}{3}$ feet of rope. If the $15\dfrac{1}{3}$ feet is divided into 4 equal pieces, how long will each piece be?

4) Bo is cutting rubber floor mats for the basement. He has $25\dfrac{1}{4}$ feet of matting. Each mat is to be $5\dfrac{1}{4}$ feet long. How many mats can be cut?

Computer Practice 7

Try this program to express improper fractions as mixed numbers. (See Appendix for more information.)

```
10    PRINT    "CONVERTING AN IMPROPER FRACTION TO A MIXED
                NUMBER"
20    INPUT    "NUMERATOR = ";A
30    INPUT    "DENOMINATOR = ";B
40    LET X = A/B
50    LET Z = INT(X) * B
60    LET Y = A - Z
70    IF Y = 0 THEN 100
80    PRINT INT(X);" AND ";Y;"/";B
90    IF Y < > 0 THEN 110
100   PRINT X
110   END
```

COMPUTER EXERCISE.   Try these improper fractions with the program.

1) $\dfrac{18}{3}$

2) $\dfrac{93}{35}$

3) $\dfrac{23}{4}$

4) $\dfrac{42}{13}$

5) $\dfrac{89}{5}$

6) $\dfrac{109}{10}$

Calculator Practice 7

Use your calculator to assist you in expressing improper fractions as mixed numbers.

Example:

Write $\dfrac{115}{25}$ as a mixed number.

Step 1: Divide the numerator by the denominator.
$115 \div 25 = 4.6$

Step 2: Multiply the whole number portion, 4, by the denominator, 25.
$25 \times 4 = 100$

Step 3: Subtract the product, 100, from 115 for the new numerator.
$115 - 100 = 15$

Solution:

$$\frac{115}{25} = 4\,\frac{15}{25}$$

CALCULATOR EXERCISE. Express these improper fractions as mixed numbers. Use your calculator to help you.

1) $\dfrac{128}{15}$

2) $\dfrac{135}{17}$

3) $\dfrac{253}{51}$

4) $\dfrac{47}{5}$

5) $\dfrac{63}{8}$

6) $\dfrac{72}{7}$

7) $\dfrac{132}{34}$

8) $\dfrac{27}{8}$

9) $\dfrac{18}{5}$

10) $\dfrac{178}{10}$

11) $\dfrac{75}{6}$

12) $\dfrac{291}{28}$

13) $\dfrac{103}{15}$

14) $\dfrac{216}{3}$

15) $\dfrac{129}{15}$

16) $\dfrac{623}{45}$

Perform the following operations. Write your answers in simplest form.

1) $12\frac{4}{5}$ 2) 16 3) $8\frac{12}{15}$ 4) $9\frac{2}{7}$

$+ 6\frac{2}{3}$ $- 3\frac{2}{5}$ $- 5\frac{1}{5}$ $- 3\frac{4}{9}$

Find the answers.

5) $5\frac{1}{5}$ ft. $\times 1\frac{1}{2}$ =

6) 7 sq. ft. $\div 1\frac{2}{5}$ =

Solve these problems. Write your answers in simplest form. Write the answers in the correct units of measure.

7) Marco used $\frac{3}{4}$ of an old shelf that was 22 inches long. How much was left over?

   a) $\frac{3}{88}$ inches

   b) $16\frac{1}{2}$ inches

   c) $5\frac{1}{2}$ inches

8) Fran measured the distance around his desk. The measurements were 26 inches, $30\frac{1}{2}$ inches, 26 inches, and $30\frac{1}{2}$ inches. Find the perimeter of Fran's desk.

9) Otto has a board $6\frac{1}{2}$ feet long. If he wants to divide the board into shelves $\frac{2}{3}$ of a foot long, how many shelves can he cut?

10) Find the area of Cara's kitchen. The length equals $12\frac{1}{2}$ feet, and the width equals 10 feet.

CHAPTER 8

SPENDING MONEY

INTRODUCTION: DECIMALS AND PLACE VALUE

To spend money wisely, a person needs to be able to read prices and to compare prices. You should be able to add the price of several items and compute the amount of change you should receive.

A smart shopper knows how much the purchases will be, which is the better buy, and how much change is due. Since money is written in decimal form, a knowledge of decimals is useful.

Example:

Identify the place value for each digit in these numbers: 2.631, $21.95

			2	.	6	3	1	
		2	1	.	9	5		

EXERCISE A.   Practice with place value. Construct a place value chart and write each number below in the proper places.

1)	12.65		9)	$2.96
2)	$.35		10)	1.035
3)	101.935		11)	0.0098
4)	$62.05		12)	105.36
5)	203.902		13)	0.009
6)	1.213		14)	0.1556
7)	$161.08		15)	0.0832
8)	516.15		16)	$1.01

Comparing Decimals. You can determine which of two given decimals is the greater by inspection. For example, compare 2.631 and 5.89. Use the less than (<) or greater than (>) *symbol.*

Since the whole number portion, 2, is less than the whole number 5, 2 < 5. Therefore, 2.631 < 5.89.

Example:

Compare .62 and .0931. Use < or >.

Step 1:   Write the numbers one over the other, lining up the decimal points.

.62
.0931

Step 2:   Add zeros so that both decimals have the same number of digits.

.6200
.0931

Step 3:   You may ignore the decimal points and think, "6200 is greater than 931."

Therefore, .62 > .0931

EXERCISE B. Compare the following decimals. Use the symbols < and >.

1) 2.35 and 2.151
2) 4.63 and 2.7
3) .562 and .9
4) .06 and .1
5) .06 and .30
6) $.05 and $.90
7) .02 and .093
8) 1.1 and .98
9) $.03 and $1
10) .0021 and .9
11) .09 and .0101
12) 3.04 and 1.2
13) 1.023 and 3.3
14) 4.021 and 9.4
15) 29.1 and 30
16) 3.09 and .9098
17) $.60 and $.08
18) $21.02 and $22
19) 3.30 and .340
20) 1 and .911

Reading Prices. Often the price on a food item does not have the dollar sign or a decimal point.

Example:

A jar of peanut butter shows a price of 295. How much does the peanut butter really cost?

Your choices are:

a) $295.00
b) $29.50
c) $2.95
d) $.295

The correct answer is c) $2.95. This is the most reasonable price.

When the decimal point has been omitted from a
price, place the decimal point two places from the right.
295 as a price means $2.95.

A can of baked beans has a price of 2/45. What does this mean?
Your choices are:

a) 2 cans for $45.00   b) 2 cans for $4.50   c) 2 cans for $.45

Use the rule. Place the decimal point two places from the right.
The correct answer is: c) 2 cans for $.45

Remember: 295 really means $2.95.
45 is really $.45 or 45¢.
3/350 is really 3/$3.50 or 3 for $3.50.

EXERCISE C.   Complete the information for this chart. Write the actual prices for each item of Brands A and B. Then, indicate which brand is cheaper. The first one has been done for you.

	Item	Brand A		Brand B		Cheaper Brand
		Price Shown	Actual Price	Price Shown	Actual Price	
1)	Beans	3/200	3/2.00	3/198	3/1.98	B
2)	Cheese	465	___	395	___	___
3)	Vinegar	99	___	89	___	___
4)	Peas	˅78	___	68	___	___
5)	Jelly	2/300	___	2/298	___	___
6)	Pickles	398	___	300	___	___
7)	Sugar	300	___	325	___	___
8)	Peppers	395	___	400	___	___
9)	Butter	250	___	349	___	___
10)	Tomatoes	125/lb.	___	100/lb.	___	___
11)	Potatoes	350/5 lb.	___	245/5 lb.	___	___
12)	Turnips	3/65	___	3/40	___	___
13)	Steak	680	___	500	___	___
14)	Rolls	198	___	97	___	___
15)	Jam	263	___	265	___	___
16)	Onions	2/99	___	2/100	___	___
17)	Apples	3/100	___	3/98	___	___
18)	Oranges	6/175	___	6/100	___	___
19)	Corn	6/175	___	6/145	___	___
20)	Beets	95 lb.	___	100 lb.	___	___

ADDITION OF DECIMALS

When you add decimals, it is important to keep the places in the same column so that you will not add tenths to hundredths. You can do this easily if you line up the decimal points. For example, to add 2.3 + .06 + 5, you would write in a column. Inserting zeros will help keep numbers in the correct column:

Examples:

Add 2.3 + .06 + 5

```
  2.3              2.30
  .06              0.06
+ 5        OR    + 5.00
——————           ——————
                  7.36
```

Add 5 + .09 + .7

```
  5                5.00
  .09              0.09
+  .7      OR    + 0.70
——————           ——————
                  5.79
```

EXERCISE A.   Write these problems in vertical form and add. Remember to line up the decimal points.

1)   6 + .35 + 2.6
2)   5.8 + 16 + .45
3)   15.61 + 1.2 + 9
4)   2 + .008 + .25

5)   3.6 + 8 + 2.35
6)   14.1 + 2 + .506
7)   8.2 + .07 + 11
8)   13.62 + 1.2 + .309

Adding Prices. Stavros went shopping for a camping trip and bought the following items. How much money did he spend for them?

Remember, the price does not always have a decimal or dollar sign. Solve this by placing the decimal point two places from the right.

Stavros's List	Price Shown	Actual Price
Baked beans	45	$ .45
Dry cereal	195	$1.95
Beef stew	250	$2.50
Tomatoes	95	$ .95
Coffee	458	+ $4.58
		$10.43

Stavros spent $10.43 for the items.

SUPERMARKET PRICES

Green Beans, 16-oz. can 3/155
Tea Bags, box of 100 279
Orange Juice, 16-oz. can 109
Onions, 3-lb. bag 99
Cat Food, 6-oz. can 58
Apple Juice, 46-oz. can 2/219
Eggs, dozen 125
Corn, pkg. of 6 ears 98
Macaroni, 16-oz. box 75
Detergent, 50-oz. box 189

EXERCISE B.   Add the prices to find the total for each order.

1)   3 cans of green beans
     1 package of corn
     3 pounds of onions

2)   1 dozen eggs
     1 box of detergent
     1 box of tea bags

3)   1 can orange juice
     1 box detergent
     1 can cat food

4)   1 box tea bags
     3 packages of corn
     3 pounds of onions

5)   1 package of corn
     1 dozen eggs
     2 cans of apple juice

6)   1 can of cat food
     4 cans of apple juice
     1 can of orange juice

7)   1 box of detergent
     1 box of tea bags
     3 cans of green beans
     1 can of cat food

8)   1 box of macaroni
     3 pounds of onions
     1 dozen eggs
     1 can of orange juice

Calculator Practice 8

When you add decimals on a calculator, remember to include any decimal points. Press the + button after each addend except the last one. You press the = button after the last addend.

Example:

2.3 ⬚ + ⬚ 5 ⬚ + ⬚ .008 ⬚ = ⬚ 7.308

CALCULATOR EXERCISE. Add these numbers on your calculator.

1)	235.06	2)	50.638	3)	2.23402
	1238.091		1.1093		.081152
	462.923		175.2063		1.120803
	2630.105		361.189		.18165
+	62.188	+	201.892	+	3.5176

Computer Practice 8

The easiest way to add decimals with a computer is to use a PRINT statement. (See Appendix for more information.)

Example:

What is the sum of 23.562, 111.89, and 78?

Type this: PRINT 23.562 + 111.89 + 78 ®
             213.452

Some advantages of adding on a computer are:
1) The larger keys are easier to use.
2) The larger display is easier to read.

COMPUTER EXERCISE.   Try adding these numbers on the computer.

1)		2)		3)	
	256.72389		.008703		1.124883
	42.0763		.523629		39.063011
	914.7203		2.079377		1.721789
	282.10035		.11654		.02302
+	.8807	+	1.441926	+	21.723419

SUBTRACTION WITH DECIMALS

When you subtract decimals, first line up the decimal points. You may have to write zeros before you can subtract. For example, if Miss Lawson bought a jacket for $87.92. How much change should she receive if she gave the salesclerk $100?

```
  $100        ← Write a decimal point and two zeros here.
-  87.92
```

```
  $100.00
-  87.92
  $ 12.08
```

EXERCISE A.   Write these subtraction problems in vertical form and sub-tract. Add any zeros that are needed.

1) $23 - $2.67
2) $50 - $1.93
3)   2.03 - .8
4)   4 - 2.09
5)   3 - .04

6)   67.9 - .341
7)   2.1 - .92
8)   24.93 - 3.4
9)   1 - .3
10)   6 - .721

EXERCISE B.   Find the amount of change due for each purchase.

	Cost	Paid With		Cost	Paid With
1)	$79.60	$100	13)	$0.54	$20
2)	$18.75	$20	14)	$39	$50
3)	$42.50	$50	15)	$567.09	$1000
4)	$39.36	$40	16)	$73.15	$100
5)	$1.59	$2	17)	$15.65	$75
6)	$42.70	$50	18)	$4.76	$10.76
7)	$11.95	$20	19)	$1.23	$2
8)	$11.76	$20	20)	$2.41	$10.01
9)	$17.36	$20.01	21)	$39.23	$50.03
10)	$9.78	$50	22)	$1.11	$20
11)	$11.90	$40	23)	$203	$500
12)	$4.02	$10.02	24)	$8.98	$20

Adding and Subtracting Money.   Both addition and subtraction of money take place when you buy more than one item at a time. For example, Amy bought a blouse for $11.95, a skirt for $17.50, and socks for $1.95. If she gave the salesclerk $50, how much change should she receive?

First you would add the items together. Then you would subtract to find the change due.

Step 1:   Add.

```
  $11.95
   17.50
+   1.95
─────────
  $31.40    ← Total
```

Step 2:   Subtract (to find the change due).

```
  $50.00
-  31.40
─────────
  $18.60    ← Change due.
```

123

EXERCISE C.   Find the amount of change due for each purchase.

Items Bought	Paid With
1) Coat, $189.95 Hat, $28.99	$300
2) Shirt, $19.99 Coat, $92.00	$200
3) Sandals, $29.95 Scarf, $12.00	$50
4) Gloves, $23.50 Dress, $52.75	$100
5) Belt, $26.50 Pants, $49.00	$100
6) Sweater, $38.25 Blouse, $52.00	$200

	Items Bought	Paid With
7)	Skirt, $21.50 Belt, $12.50 Shoes, $44.99 Hat, $16.00	$100
8)	Shorts, $24.80 Blouse, $48.75 Socks, $6.00 Shoes, $69.10	$200
9)	Slippers, $19.50 Socks, $3.50 Skirt, $23.90 Blouse, $25.99	$100
10)	Suit, $395.00 Vest, $49.95 Belt, $28.00 Shirt, $50.00	$1000

CHAPTER TEST

What is the place value of each underlined digit?

1) $2̲1.65   3) .35̲   5) $26̲.72   7) $12̲.096

2) 3.0̲15   4) $1.6035̲   6) $2̲31.72   8) $36.21̲

Write *True* or *False* for each of these comparisons.

9) .091 > 1.1   10) .035 < .10   11) .01 > .0098

Write these prices correctly with decimal points.

12) Tomatoes, cans ....2/87   13) Peanut butter, jar 179

Find the total amount of each purchase.

14) Cooking oil   175
    Baked beans   45
    10 lbs. potatoes   279

15) Frozen dinner   159
    Canned corn   55
    Lettuce   75

Find the amount of change due.

16) Coat, $29.95—Paid $50

17) Shoes, $19.11—Paid $25

Perform the indicated operations.

18) $2.50 + $.85 + $30   20) $29 - $.89

19) 5.6 + .28 + 5 + .6   21) 1.1 - .063

Find the total cost and the amount of change due for each set of purchases.

	Items Bought	Paid With		Items Bought	Paid With
22)	Hat, $49.00 Gloves, $29.95 Shoes, $88.95	$200	24)	Sweater, $55.60 Vest, $32.00 Scarf, $22.00	$150
23)	Slippers, $35.00 Shirt, $31.99 Ribbon, $6.00	$100	25)	Suit, $250.00 Belt, $19.00 Shoes, $42.00	$400

CHAPTER 9

EARNING MONEY

Everyone wants to have enough money to do the things that they like to do. Most of us need to work to earn that money. Our job will earn us a certain amount of money per hour worked. After we have worked a certain number of hours, we are paid. The total is referred to as *gross pay*. Our gross pay is our hourly pay times the number of hours worked. Gross pay is your pay before *deductions*. Deductions include state and federal taxes and Social Security. After all deductions have been made, the result is your *net pay*.

We know how much we expect to be paid if we multiply the hourly pay by the number of hours worked. The mathematical skill used here is multiplying money, a two place decimal, by a whole number. Let's practice this skill.

Multiply:

| 1) | $2.85 × 32 | 2) | $3.16 × 24 | 3) | $4.12 × 16 | 4) | $4.38 × 35 | 5) | $5.14 × 26 |

MULTIPLICATION OF DECIMALS

We multiply decimals to compute the gross pay earned by a worker who gets paid by the hour. For example, Greg worked part time as a bricklayer's helper and earned $3.75 per hour. If he worked 35 hours during a one-week period, how much was his gross pay for that week?

Multiply the hourly wage by the number of hours worked.

$$
\begin{array}{r}
\$3.75 \quad \leftarrow 2 \text{ places} \\
\times \quad 35 \quad \leftarrow 0 \text{ places} \\
\hline
18\,75 \\
112\,5 \quad\;\; \\
\hline
\$131.25 \quad \leftarrow 2 + 0 = 2 \text{ places}
\end{array}
$$

Since there are two decimal places in the factors, we count off two decimal places in the product.

Greg's gross pay was $131.25.

Marti earned $4.50 per hour with her part time job after school. If she worked 8 hours during a one-week period, how much did she earn?

$$
\begin{array}{r}
\$4.50 \\
\times \quad 8 \\
\hline
\$36.00
\end{array}
$$

The total number of places to the right of the decimals determines the number of places in the answer.

Marti earned $36.00.

EXERCISE A.   Find the gross pay for these workers.

1)   32 hours at $4.75 per hour.
2)   17 hours at $4.19 per hour.
3)   22 hours at $5.25 per hour.

EXERCISE B.   Find the answers by multiplying.

1)   Heather worked part time as a shoe salesperson and earned $6.40 per hour. She worked an 11-hour week. Find her weekly gross earnings.

2)   Nelson worked an 8-hour week earning $5.90 per hour as a carpenter's helper. What was Nelson's gross pay each week?

3)   June's part time job earned her $6.55 per hour as a stock clerk. How much did June earn if she worked 22 hours?

4)   The Super Food Market paid $6.10 per hour for a person to stock shelves. How much would a person earn at this job working 15 hours?

5)   Anderson tutored after school and earned $4.75 per hour. If he worked 6 hours a week, how much did he earn per week?

EXERCISE C.   Find the gross pay.

1)	30 hours at $4.50 per hour	12)	28 hours at $7.16 per hour	23)	36 hours at $7.60 per hour
2)	22 hours at $5.60 per hour	13)	32 hours at $4.00 per hour	24)	40 hours at $8.00 per hour
3)	15 hours at $5.75 per hour	14)	23 hours at $4.95 per hour	25)	9 hours at $3.10 per hour
4)	28 hours at $4.50 per hour	15)	31 hours at $7.18 per hour	26)	42 hours at $9.20 per hour
5)	16 hours at $4.00 per hour	16)	42 hours at $4.25 per hour	27)	40 hours at $4.60 per hour
6)	19 hours at $5.65 per hour	17)	25 hours at $4.25 per hour	28)	5 hours at $4.95 per hour
7)	23 hours at $7.75 per hour	18)	16 hours at $5.50 per hour	29)	29 hours at $4.95 per hour
8)	36 hours at $8.25 per hour	19)	15 hours at $7.50 per hour	30)	19 hours at $6.75 per hour
9)	12 hours at $4.95 per hour	20)	8 hours at $5.60 per hour	31)	14 hours at $5.50 per hour
10)	17 hours at $5.00 per hour	21)	5 hours at $2.20 per hour	32)	39 hours at $7.10 per hour
11)	11 hours at $4.65 per hour	22)	38 hours at $6.50 per hour	33)	13 hours at $4.80 per hour

Multiplying Decimals by Decimals. When multiplying decimals it is not necessary to line up the decimals. The placement of the decimal point in the answer is determined by the total number of places to the right of the decimal point in each factor.

Examples:

When you see this:

$2.65 \times 1.5 =$

Write it this way:

```
  2.65    ← 2 places
×  1.5    ← 1 place
 1 325
 2 65
 3.975    ← 3 places
```

When you see this:

$.203 \times .04 =$

You write this:

```
  .203    ← 3 places
× .04     ← 2 places
.00812    ← 5 places
```

EXERCISE D. Multiply these decimals. Count the decimal places in each problem before you place the decimal point in the answer.

1) $3.25
    ×   1.5

2) $4.20
    ×   16

3) $1.95
    ×   .28

4)   5.56
    × 3.2

5)   .063
    × 2.9

6)   1.03
    × .99

7) $2.60
    ×   1.5

8)   .68
    × 2.5

9)   735
    × 5.2

10) 1.69
    ×   13

11) 52.33
    × 2.3

12) .263
    × .09

13)   .087
    ×   .06

14)   7.31
    × 1.06

15) .2106
    ×   .35

16) .0528
    × .003

17)   .002
    ×   .03

18) 1.006
    × 1.07

19)   3.15
    ×   .16

20)   .819
    ×   23

21)   5.1
    ×   .06

22)   .205
    ×   .01

23)   2.68
    ×   10

24) $4.78
    × 100

Multiplying with Decimal Parts of an Hour. The number of hours an employee works may not always be a whole number. The worker may get paid for $\frac{1}{4}$, $\frac{1}{2}$, or $\frac{3}{4}$ of an hour.

Examples:

Mark worked $11\frac{1}{2}$ hours after school earning $2.25 per hour. How much was his gross pay? (Remember: $11\frac{1}{2} = 11.5$)

$$
\begin{array}{r}
\$2.25 \quad \leftarrow 2 \text{ places} \\
\times \quad 11.5 \quad \leftarrow 1 \text{ place} \\
\hline
1\ 125 \\
2\ 25 \\
22\ 5 \\
\hline
\$25.875 \quad \leftarrow 3 \text{ places}
\end{array}
$$

Since only 2 decimal places are needed for money, we round off the gross pay to the nearest cent.

Mark's gross pay was $25.88.

Alice worked as a waitress and earned $4.57 per hour. If she worked $12\frac{1}{4}$ hours for one week, how much was her gross pay? (Remember: $12\frac{1}{4} = 12.25$)

$$
\begin{array}{r}
12.25 \quad \text{Hours} \\
\times \quad \$4.57 \quad \text{Per hour} \\
\hline
8575 \\
6\ 125 \\
49\ 00 \\
\hline
\$55.9825 \quad \text{Gross pay}
\end{array}
$$

Remember, only two places are used for money.
$55.9825 \approx $55.98
Alice's gross pay was $55.98.

Phillip worked $10\frac{3}{4}$ hours for an hourly pay of $3.29. Find his gross pay.
(Remember: $10\frac{3}{4} = 10.75$)

```
    10.75    ← 2 places
 ×  $3.29    ← 2 places
    9675
   2 150
  32 25
 $35.3675  ≈  $35.37
```

Phillip's gross pay was $35.37.

EXERCISE E.   Find the gross pay.

1)   Stella worked $11\frac{1}{2}$ hours earning $3.25 per hour. Find Stella's gross pay.

2)   Jose earned $4.26 per hour as a tutor after school. Find his gross pay if he worked $9\frac{1}{4}$ hours.

3)   Kim was an assistant clerk at City Hospital. She earned $4.20 an hour. She worked $36\frac{3}{4}$ hours in one week. How much was her gross pay?

4)   Mandy worked as an electrician's helper, earning $5.25 per hour. If she worked $28\frac{3}{4}$ hours in one week, how much was her gross pay?

5)   The Pizza Parlor pays the pizza maker $4.86 per hour. Find the gross pay if the work week is $38\frac{1}{4}$ hours.

6)   Scott earns $2.19 per hour with a babysitting service. Find his gross pay if he works 17 hours.

7)   Casey worked as a part time housecleaner 7 hours on Friday and $7\frac{1}{2}$ hours on Saturday. Find her gross pay if she earned $2.15 per hour.

EXERCISE F. Find the gross pay.

1) $30\frac{1}{2}$ hours at
$2.65 per hour

2) $15\frac{1}{2}$ hours at
$1.92 per hour

3) $6\frac{3}{4}$ hours at
$7.25 per hour

4) $12\frac{1}{2}$ hours at
$4.12 per hour

5) $13\frac{1}{2}$ hours at
$6.25 per hour

6) $10\frac{3}{4}$ hours at
$3.00 per hour

7) 5 hours at
$4.13 per hour

8) $27\frac{1}{2}$ hours at
$1.70 per hour

9) $4\frac{3}{4}$ hours at
$6.10 per hour

10) $15\frac{1}{2}$ hours at
$8.70 per hour

11) $23\frac{1}{2}$ hours at
$4.36 per hour

12) $26\frac{1}{2}$ hours at
$3.90 per hour

13) $39\frac{1}{4}$ hours at
$1.75 per hour

14) $25\frac{3}{4}$ hours at
$2.62 per hour

15) $10\frac{1}{4}$ hours at
$.93 per hour

16) $22\frac{1}{2}$ hours at
$1.50 per hour

17) $19\frac{1}{4}$ hours at
$2.50 per hour

18) $32\frac{1}{4}$ hours at
$7.25 per hour

19) $8\frac{3}{4}$ hours at
$3.73 per hour

20) $40\frac{1}{4}$ hours at
$3.95 per hour

21) $40\frac{1}{4}$ hours at
$3.76 per hour

22) $14\frac{3}{4}$ hours at
$.75 per hour

23) $21\frac{1}{4}$ hours at
$4.35 per hour

24) $28\frac{1}{4}$ hours at
$2.75 per hour

Overtime Earnings. Workers earn more than their hourly rate of pay when their employers ask them to work longer than the agreed-upon, or "straight," time. Overtime may be paid at the rate of *time and one-half* or *double-time*. *Example:*

Gary worked 43 hours at $3.19 per hour with time and one-half for all time worked over 40 hours. What was his gross pay?

Step 1: Separate straight time from overtime.

43	Total time
- 40	Agreed straight time
3	Overtime

Step 2: Convert 3 hours to time and one-half.

1.5	1.5 equals $1\frac{1}{2}$
× 3	Hours to be converted
4.5	Time and one-half

Step 3: Add straight time to time and one-half.

40	
+ 4.5	
44.5	Time used to compute gross pay

Step 4: Multiply the total time by the rate per hour.

44.5	Hours
× 3.19	Rate per hour

$141.955 \approx $141.96

Gary's gross pay was $141.96.

EXERCISE G.   Find the gross pay, including time and one-half.

1) Carol worked 44 hours at $5.20 per hour with time and one-half for all time over 40 hours. Find Carol's gross pay.

2) Ricardo worked 44 hours at $10.00 per hour with time and one-half for all time over 40 hours. Find Ricardo's gross pay.

3) Alexandra worked 9 hours at $5.25 per hour with time and one-half for all time over 8 hours. Find Alexandra's gross pay.

4) Compute the gross pay for Cindy's 46-hour work week if she gets $4.60 per hour and time and one-half for all time over 40 hours.

5) Twelve hours at $7.50 per hour with overtime after 8 hours.

6) Forty-five hours at $4.00 per hour with overtime after 40 hours.

7) Fifteen hours at $4.25 per hour with overtime after 8 hours.

8) Thirty-seven hours at $5.00 per hour with overtime after 3 hours.

9) Forty-one and one-half hours at $3.80 per hour with overtime after 40 hours.

10) Forty-two and three-fourths hours at $2.50 per hour with overtime after 40 hours.

Double Time Earnings. To find double time earnings, we first multiply the overtime hours by 2.
Example:

Holly worked 43 hours at a rate of $3.75 per hour for one week. She was paid straight time for 40 hours and double time for the time over 40 hours. What was her gross pay?

Step 1: Separate straight time from double time.

43	Total time
- 40	Agreed straight time
3	Hours at the double time rate

Step 2: Convert 3 hours to double time. To double, we multiply by 2.

3	Hours to be converted
× 2	
6	Hours

Step 3: Add straight time to double time.

$$
\begin{array}{rl}
40 & \text{Hours straight time} \\
+\ 6 & \text{Hours double time} \\
\hline
46 & \text{Total hours}
\end{array}
$$

Step 4: Multiply the rate per hour and the total.

$$
\begin{array}{rl}
\$3.75 & \text{Per hour} \\
\times\ \ \ 46 & \text{Total hours} \\
\hline
\$172.50 & \text{Gross pay}
\end{array}
$$

Holly's gross pay was $172.50.

EXERCISE H.   Find the gross pay, including double time.

1) Find Luke's pay for 48 hours if he earns $8.20 per hour with double time for any hours over 40.

2) Marconi, a plumber's helper, worked 45 hours one week. He earned $6.78 an hour, with five of the 45 hours at double time. Find Marconi's gross pay.

3) Pam earns $1.75 an hour babysitting. If she works 16 hours per week and charges double time for any time over 10 hours, how much will her gross pay be?

4) Thirteen hours at $2.26 per hour with double time over 10 hours.

5) Eighteen hours at $7.30 per hour with double time over 10 hours.

6) Forty-seven hours at $4.10 per hour with double time over 40 hours.

7) Fifty-two hours at $9.00 per hour with double time over 40 hours.

8) Twenty-six hours at $3.95 per hour with double time over 20 hours.

9) Forty-nine hours at $5.75 per hour with double time over 40 hours.

10) Nine and one-half hours at $3.00 per hour with double time over 8 hours.

11) Forty and one-half hours at $10.50 per hour with double time over 40 hours.

12) Ten and one-half hours at $4.00 per hour with double time over 8 hours.

13) Thirteen and one-half hours at $5.25 per hour with double time over 8 hours.

DIVISION OF DECIMALS

When you divide a decimal by a whole number, you divide as though you were dividing whole numbers. After you have found the quotient, you bring the decimal point straight up into the quotient.

Example:

$136.80 ÷ 30 =

```
          $4.56
30 ) $136.80
     120
     ───
     168
     150
     ───
      180
      180
      ───
```

If the divisor is a decimal, follow these steps:

Step 1: Move the decimal point in the divisor to the right of the number.

Step 2: Move the decimal point in the dividend the same number of places to the right.

Step 3: Divide and bring the decimal point up into the quotient.

.0945 ÷ 1.5 =

```
        .063
1.5 ).0945
      90
      ──
      45
      45
      ──
```

EXERCISE A.   Find the quotients.

1) 157.5 ÷ 42	7) .00558 ÷ .06
2) 35.28 ÷ 18	8) .00736 ÷ .008
3) 11.256 ÷ 2.8	9) 156.4 ÷ 34
4) 88 ÷ 3.2	10) .01943 ÷ .67
5) .08052 ÷ .61	11) 5.848 ÷ 8.5
6) .23427 ÷ .57	12) 15.75 ÷ .35

Dividing the Annual Salary. Sometimes the annual salary for a job is quoted in a want ad or in a job description. To find the weekly salary, divide the annual salary by the number of weeks worked.

Example:

Monica is paid $10,674 per year working as a typist. Find Monica's weekly salary if she works 52 weeks per year.

$$
\begin{array}{r}
\$205.269 \quad\approx\quad \$205.27 \\
52\,\overline{)\$10674.000} \\
\underline{104} \\
274 \\
\underline{260} \\
140 \\
\underline{104} \\
360 \\
\underline{312} \\
480 \\
\underline{468}
\end{array}
$$

Divide to 3 decimal places and round to the nearest cent.

Monica works 52 weeks a year. She gets paid $205.27 per week.

EXERCISE B.   For each annual salary below, find the amount paid weekly. There are 52 weeks in a year.

1)	$12,938	16)	$12,750
2)	$12,850	17)	$25,655
3)	$15,652	18)	$20,852
4)	$10,084	19)	$11,672
5)	$21,372	20)	$14,312
6)	$16,744	21)	$22,880
7)	$14,482	22)	$13,670
8)	$10,920	23)	$17,151
9)	$9,100	24)	$17,524
10)	$14,981	25)	$14,222
11)	$9,777	26)	$20,000
12)	$10,868	27)	$13,468
13)	$15,226	28)	$15,575
14)	$16,412	29)	$18,710
15)	$11,856	30)	$19,623

Dividing Gross Pay. You can find the hourly rate when you know the gross pay. Divide the gross pay by the number of hours worked.

Example:

Vernon's weekly gross pay was $150. If he worked 40 hours, what was his hourly rate?

```
            $3.75
   40 ) $150.00
         120
         300
         280
         200
         200
```

Vernon's hourly rate was $3.75.

EXERCISE C. Find the hourly rates.

	Gross Pay	Hours Worked		Gross Pay	Hours Worked
1)	$180.00	40	16)	$161.28	32
2)	$38.40	16	17)	$45.60	12
3)	$39.68	16	18)	$152.64	24
4)	$90.00	20	19)	$44.99	11
5)	$77.00	22	20)	$65.44	16
6)	$131.25	25	21)	$77.40	30
7)	$86.25	25	22)	$72.00	18
8)	$74.16	18	23)	$116.80	32
9)	$108.40	40	24)	$79.20	40
10)	$102.80	20	25)	$78.50	25
11)	$85.68	24	26)	$77.00	22
12)	$93.75	15	27)	$67.26	38
13)	$78.54	22	28)	$133.65	33
14)	$200.00	40	29)	$39.60	8
15)	$45.98	11	30)	$81.00	18

Calculator Practice 9

You may use a calculator to convert a weekly salary to an annual salary.

Example:

$225 weekly for 52 weeks = ? annual salary

225 × 52 = 11700, or $11,700.00 annual salary

CALCULATOR EXERCISE. Convert each weekly salary to an annual salary.

1)	$255.00	5)	$256.79	9)	$201.00
2)	$289.50	6)	$273.39	10)	$258.00
3)	$205.00	7)	$250.00	11)	$299.96
4)	$270.00	8)	$279.00	12)	$323.35

Computer Practice 9

If you know the hourly rate and hours worked, you may use this program to compute weekly earnings and yearly earnings. To stop program type "0" for number of hours worked. (See Appendix for more information.)

```
10    PRINT   "CONVERTING AN HOURLY RATE OF PAY TO WEEKLY
                 AND YEARLY EARNINGS"
20    INPUT "HOURS WORKED IN WEEK = ";H
30    INPUT "PAY PER HOUR = $";P
40    IF H = 0 THEN 100
50    X = H * P
60    Y = X * 52
70    PRINT "WEEKLY PAY IS $";X
80    PRINT "YEARLY PAY IS $";Y
90    GOTO 20
100   END
```

COMPUTER EXERCISE.   Use these hourly rates in the program above.

1)	3.45	11)	4.90
2)	4.65	12)	3.70
3)	3.62	13)	5.45
4)	4.40	14)	8.72
5)	5.95	15)	5.65
6)	3.65	16)	3.90
7)	5.85	17)	4.30
8)	3.90	18)	6.25
9)	3.80	19)	5.09
10)	4.45	20)	5.90

REVIEW EXERCISE A.   Find the gross pay.

1)   5 hrs., $2.60 an hour

2)   8 hrs., $9.50 an hour

3)   18 hrs., $8.50 an hour

4)   38 hrs., $3.40 an hour

5)   40 hrs., $4.20 an hour

6)   32 hrs., $4.60 an hour

7)   9 hrs., $5.75 an hour

8)   25 hrs., $3.90 an hour

9)   Twelve hours at $11.75 an hour with time and one-half after 8 hours.

10)   Sixteen hours at $9.50 an hour with time and one-half after 10 hours.

11)   Forty-three hours at $14.00 an hour with time and one-half after 40 hours.

12)   Forty-eight hours at $10.75 an hour with double time after 40 hours.

13)   Ten hours at $4.67 an hour with double time after 8 hours.

REVIEW EXERCISE B.   Complete the information for these charts.

Annual Salary	Weekly Salary
1) $13,405	____
2) $14,260	____
3) $15,486	____
4) $16,810	____
5) $10,676	____
6) $18,582	____

Gross Pay	Hours Worked	Hourly Rate
7) $145.20	40	____
8) $104	32	____
9) $174.80	38	____
10) $46.80	30	____
11) $43.20	9	____
12) $95.85	27	____

CHAPTER TEST

Find the products.
1) 2.78 × .36
2) .076 × .09
3) 2.9 × .19

Find the gross pay.
4) Thirty-five hours at $9.25 per hour
5) Six hours at $8.75 per hour
6) Three hours at $4.15 per hour
7) Ten and one-fourth hours at $3.75 per hour
8) Twelve and one-half hours at $5.20 per hour
9) Eighteen and three-fourths hours at $4.10 per hour
10) Forty-four hours at $7.10 an hour with time and one-half after 40 hours
11) Forty-five hours at $7.25 per hour with time and one-half after 40 hours
12) Eighteen hours at $15.00 per hour with double time after 40 hours
13) Forty-six hours at $8.90 an hour with double time after 40 hours

Divide. Round the quotient to the nearest hundredth.
14) 72.96 ÷ 48
15) .1152 ÷ 6.4
16) .00144 ÷ .08

Convert each annual salary to a weekly salary.
17) $15,083
18) $12,375.50

Convert each weekly gross pay to an hourly rate.
19) $124.20 for 36 hours
20) $161.85 for 39 hours

CHAPTER 10

TRAVELING

You use decimals when traveling. Decimals are used to measure the distance that you drive, the amount of gas you buy, your *mileage*, and the cost of your hotel room.

When you add or subtract decimals, you must line up the decimal points. Bring the decimal point straight down to your answer.

Examples:

$3.46 + .298 + 45 = ?$

$$\begin{array}{r} 3.46 \\ .298 \\ + \quad 45 \\ \hline 48.758 \end{array}$$

$45.6 - 2.86 = ?$

$$\begin{array}{r} 45.60 \quad \leftarrow \text{Zero added} \\ - \quad 2.86 \\ \hline 42.74 \end{array}$$

Remember to think of the decimal point as being to the right of a whole number.

EXERCISE A. Rewrite in vertical form and find the sums or differences.

1) 2.306 + 61.9
2) 28.234 - 6.48
3) .125 + 3.8 + 4.35
4) 52 + 31.6 + 2.434
5) .46 - .203
6) .306 + .7 + .1246
7) 53 - .869
8) 8.032 - .17
9) 3.6 + 36 + .036
10) 356.9 - 268.83

When you multiply, you must count the number of decimal places in the problem in order to determine the number of decimal places in the answer. When you divide, you may need to rewrite the problem so that the divisor is a whole number.

Examples:

$2.32 \times .126 = ?$

```
    2.32      ← 2 places
×   .126      ← 3 places
    1392
    464
    232
   .29232     ← 5 places
```

$14.72 \div 4.6 = ?$

```
                    3.2
4.6 )14.72     46 )147.2
                   138
                    9 2
                    9 2
```

EXERCISE B.   Rewrite each problem in the proper form and find the product or quotient.

1)   4.8 × .36
2)   12.22 ÷ 26
3)   17.92 ÷ 3.2
4)   .121 × .106
5)   528 ÷ 1.5
6)   .4 ÷ 25
7)   456 × 2.8
8)   58.8 ÷ 35
9)   .0042 × .037
10)   5673 × .48

ODOMETER READING

An *odometer* measures how far a car has traveled. It measures this distance in tenths of a mile. The odometer is found on the *speedometer* of the car.

Example:

At the beginning of the trip, the odometer read:

5 2 8 7 6	3

At the end of the trip, the odometer read:

5 3 9 1 0	1

Subtract to find how many miles were driven.

```
   53910.1
-  52876.3
   1033.8
```

The total distance traveled was 1033.8 miles.

EXERCISE A.   Answer these questions about odometer readings.

1) At the beginning of Susan's vacation, she noticed that the odometer in her car read 46892 5 . When she returned the odometer read 47325 7 . How far did she drive?

2) When Sam left home, his odometer read 06729 2 . It read 10040 8 when Sam arrived in Macon, Georgia. How far had he driven?

3) While driving Stacy saw a sign that said, "Dallas—189 miles." He glanced at his odometer and saw that it read 38876 3 . What will it read when Stacy gets to Dallas?

4) Todd is going to the beach for the day. The beach is 48.7 miles away. If the odometer reads 62984 5 when he leaves, what will it read when Todd arrives at the beach?

5) When Barbara left for work in the morning, her odometer read 37928 3 . It read 37953 1 when she arrived. How far does she drive to work?

Calculator Practice 10

CALCULATOR EXERCISE. Use your calculator to find the miles traveled.

Trip Begins With:	Trip Ends With:	Miles Traveled
1) 72155.7	72389.2	____
2) 69016.1	69143.0	____
3) 28823.8	29002.0	____
4) 31057.8	33850.4	____
5) 89163.1	90014.3	____
6) 30062.5	32145.9	____
7) 29915.1	31304.5	____

GAS MILEAGE

You can use your odometer to help compute your gas mileage. This is the number of miles that you can expect to travel on one gallon of gas.

To compute your gas mileage, follow these steps:

Step 1: Fill your gas tank and record the odometer reading.

Step 2: The next time that you buy gas, fill the tank again. Record the number of gallons of gas that you bought and the odometer reading.

Step 3: Subtract the two odometer readings to find the number of miles driven.

Step 4: Divide this answer by the number of gallons of gas that you just bought. Round to the nearest whole number.

Example:

Reading at second filling   36982.8

Reading at first filling   - 36784.3

 198.5

$$7.3 \overline{)198.50}$$ 27.1 $\approx$ 27 miles to the gallon

EXERCISE A.   Compute the gas mileage each driver gets.

Reading When Tank Was Filled	Gallons of Gas Bought	Reading at Second Filling	Gas Mileage
1) 43872.5	6.2	44075.2	——
2) 39989.6	9.2	40230.3	——
3) 56035.3	10.3	56398.5	——
4) 87392.7	8.4	87631.6	——
5) 21981.3	7.6	22160.1	——
6) 70384.3	9.3	70699.2	——
7) 06721.9	8.9	06997.9	——
8) 13297.2	7.2	13491.6	——
9) 00428.4	8.4	00779.6	——
10) 66879.2	8.1	67041.0	——

GASOLINE EXPENSES

The cost of an automobile trip can be found by multiplying the number of gallons of gasoline used times the cost per gallon. Round the cost to the nearest cent.

Example:
Find the total cost of 12.3 gallons of gasoline used at $1.49 per gallon.

```
      1.49      Cost per gallon
  ×  12.3       Number of gallons
  ———————
      447
      298
      149
  ———————
  $18.327    ≈   $18.33
```

$18.33 is the total cost.

EXERCISE A.   Find the total cost of gasoline. Round to the nearest cent.

1)	1.6 gallons at $1.45	14)	50 gallons at $1.25
2)	25.1 gallons at $1.65	15)	42.9 gallons at $1.53
3)	1.1 gallons at $1.42	16)	31.5 gallons at $1.38
4)	80 gallons at $1.40	17)	43.2 gallons at $1.62
5)	26.7 gallons at $1.35	18)	4.6 gallons at $1.76
6)	3.3 gallons at $1.52	19)	37.7 gallons at $1.53
7)	18.4 gallons at $1.75	20)	42.9 gallons at $1.45
8)	27.5 gallons at $1.28	21)	2.9 gallons at $1.65
9)	27.4 gallons at $1.11	22)	31.4 gallons at $1.50
10)	52.5 gallons at $1.49	23)	17.5 gallons at $1.77
11)	3.5 gallons at $1.32	24)	10.8 gallons at $1.80
12)	39 gallons at $1.78	25)	1.6 gallons at $1.98
13)	3.2 gallons at $1.28	26)	12.3 gallons at $1.22

Computer Practice 10

Use this program to compute the total cost of gasoline. (See Appendix for more information.)

```
10     REM COMPUTING THE COST OF GASOLINE
20     PRINT "ENTER THE COST PER GALLON"
30     PRINT "TO STOP PROGRAM ENTER 0"
40     INPUT C
50     IF C = 0 THEN 100
60     PRINT "ENTER NUMBER OF GALLONS"
70     INPUT N
80     PRINT "THE TOTAL COST IS $";
90     PRINT N * C
100    END
```

Example: Enter 12 gallons at $1.55 per gallon.
TYPE 1.55 without the $ SYMBOL for the cost per gallon.
TYPE 12 for the number of gallons.

The answer will be 18.6 or $18.60.

COMPUTER EXERCISE.   Find the total cost of gasoline. Round to the nearest cent.

1)   16 gallons at $1.65
2)   25 gallons at $1.60
3)   35 gallons at $2.50
4)   95 gallons at $1.42
5)   62 gallons at $1.32
6)   46 gallons at $1.40
7)   76 gallons at $1.72
8)   53 gallons at $1.12

9)   82 gallons at $1.51
10)   96 gallons at $1.62
11)   63 gallons at $1.29
12)   84 gallons at $1.99
13)   102 gallons at $1.45
14)   98 gallons at $2.01
15)   45 gallons at $2.21
16)   61 gallons at $2.32

CAR RENTAL RATES

Some travelers need to *rent* a car. Rental rates differ for different sized cars.

Type of Car	Per Day	Per Week	Plus per Mile
Subcompact	$13.50	$ 72.50	14¢
Compact	$18.95	$120.00	16¢
Mid-sized	$23.95	$151.00	18¢
Large	$35.95	$231.50	20¢
Van	$45.95	$295.00	22¢

EXERCISE A.   Use the chart of car rental rates to answer these questions.

1)   How much does it cost to rent a mid-sized car for one day if you drive it 127 miles?

2)   Hilary rented a compact car for one week. She drove it 628 miles. What was the cost?

3)   Audrey rented a van for four days. What was the charge if she drove the car 473 miles?

4) How much would it have cost Audrey if she had rented a compact car instead of the van?

5) How much would Audrey have saved if she had rented the compact car instead of the van?

6) What did Bob pay to rent a large car for two weeks if he drove 473 miles?

7) Kim rented a subcompact car for four days. She drove 608 miles. How much did Kim pay?

8) Juan drove the mid-sized car that he rented 462 miles. How much did Juan pay if he rented the car for three days?

USING A MAP

Using a map to compute distances traveled often requires the use of basic mathematical operations.

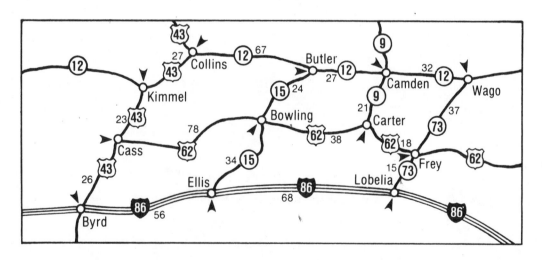

Key

o .... Town

(6) .... State Route

(82) .... U.S. Highway

(21) .... Interstate Highway

24 ..... Mileage Between Arrows

Example:

If you drive from Camden to Bowling on 9 and 62, you will travel 21 + 38, or 59 miles.

If you average 35 miles per hour, what will your travel time be?

Divide by 35 and round to nearest tenth.

$$
\begin{array}{r}
1.68 \approx 1.7 \text{ hours} \\
35 \overline{)59.00} \\
\underline{35} \\
240 \\
\underline{210} \\
300 \\
\underline{280}
\end{array}
$$

EXERCISE A.   Use the road map to answer the questions.   Round any remainders to one decimal place.

1) How far will you drive if you go from Butler to Cass along ⑮ and ⑯²?

2) If you average 42 miles per hour, how long will this trip take?

3) You drove from Lobelia to Bowling along 🛡86 and ⑮. How far did you drive?

4) If the trip from Lobelia to Bowling took 2.3 hours, what was the average rate of speed?

5) What is the distance from Byrd to Frey along 🛡86 and ⑦³?

6) If you average 52 miles per hour, how long will it take you to make this trip?

7) How far is it from Camden to Cass along ⑨ and ⑯²?

8) How far is it from Camden to Cass along ⑫ and ⑭³?

9) If you go from Camden to Cass along ⑨ and ⑯², you can average 37 miles per hour. If you use ⑫ and ⑭³, you can average 42 miles per hour. Which route takes less time?

10) How far is it from Kimmel to Lobelia along ⑭³ and 🛡86?

GAS CONSUMPTION

Gas mileage is found by dividing the distance traveled by the gallons of gas used. If you know the number of miles that you get to a gallon of gas, you can predict the amount of gas that you will use to drive a given distance. You would divide the distance by the miles per gallon.

Examples:

Drove 143 miles and
used 4.3 gallons of gas.

```
        33.25   ≈  33.3 miles per gallon
4.3 ) 143.000
      129
      ----
      140
      129
      ----
      110
       86
      ----
      240
      215
      ----
```

Drove 206 miles and
got 32 miles per gallon.

```
       6.43   ≈   6.4 gallons of gas
32 ) 206.00
     192
     ----
     140
     128
     ----
     120
      96
```

EXERCISE A.   Use the map on page 153 to answer these questions about gasoline consumption. Round any remainders to one decimal place.

1)   You used 3.2 gallons of gas to go from Collins to Carter along ⑫ and ⑨. What was your gas mileage?

2)   You drove from Ellis to Wago along 🛡86 and ⑦3. If your car gets 31 miles to the gallon of gas, how many gallons did you use?

3)   You drove from Cass to Lobelia and used 5.2 gallons of gas. What was your mileage? You drove along 🛡62 and ⑦3.

4)   You used 3.9 gallons of gas to drive from Carter to Byrd along 🛡62, ⑮, and 🛡86. What was your mileage?

5)   How many gallons of gas will you use to drive from Bowling to Collins along ⑫ and ⑮ if your car gets 34 miles per gallon?

6)   You drove from Frey to Cass along 🛡62. How many gallons of gas did you use if your car gets 28 miles per gallon?

7)   You used 3.5 gallons of gas to drive from Camden to Ellis along ⑨, 🛡62, and ⑮. What was your gas mileage?

8)   Your car gets 36 miles per gallon. How many gallons of gas would you use to drive from Collins to Frey along ⑫, ⑮, and 🛡62 ?

HOTEL RATES

Hotel rates are given as the cost for each person.

Hotel Length of Stay	Room Type	Single	Extra Night	Double Cost for Each	Extra Night
Seaside Inn					
3 Nights	Standard	113.25	36.25	65.25	20.25
	Deluxe	137.25	44.25	77.25	24.25
7 Nights	Standard	257.25	36.25	145.25	20.25
	Deluxe	313.25	44.25	173.25	24.25
Bay Hotel					
3 Nights	Superior	80.30	25.30	51.80	15.80
7 Nights	Superior	180.30	25.30	113.80	15.80
Forest Lodge					
3 Nights	Standard	131.35	42.35	71.35	22.35
7 Nights	Standard	299.35	42.35	159.35	22.35

Example:

Mr. and Mrs. Myers are spending three nights at the Seaside Inn in a deluxe double room. The cost is 2 × $77.25, or $154.50.

EXERCISE A.   Use this rate chart to answer the questions.

1) How much will it cost for Elise to spend seven nights at the Forest Lodge in a single room?

2) Judy and Jean are going to spend seven nights in a standard room at the Seaside Inn. What will the total cost be if they share a double room?

3) How much will it cost to spend four nights in a single room at the Bay Hotel?

4) How much will it cost Pat and Lee Scott to stay for eight nights at the Bay Hotel?

5) A travel agent arranged for a group of 38 people to stay for three nights. They are all staying in double rooms. Twelve people are staying at the Seaside Inn in deluxe rooms; 16 at the Forest Lodge; and 10 at the Bay Hotel. What is the total bill?

CURRENCY CONVERSION

If you are traveling outside of our country, you will need to change from United States currency to another country's currency. To do this, multiply by the *conversion factor*. To change from another country's currency to United States currency, divide by the conversion factor.

Country	Currency	Conversion Factor 1 U.S. Dollar =
Barbados	Barbados dollar = 100 cents	1.96 BDD
Bermuda	Bermudan dollar = 100 cents	1.00 BED
Cayman Is.	Cayman Is. dollar = 100 cents	.85 CID
Cuba	Cuban peso = 100 centavos	.83 CUP
Haiti	Gourde = 100 centimes	5.00 GOU
Jamaica	Jamaican dollar = 100 cents	1.79 JAD
Trinidad	Trinidad dollar = 100 cents	2.35 TTD
West Indies	East Carib dollar = 100 cents	1.85 ECD

Examples:

Change 40 U.S. dollars to Barbados currency.

```
  1.96
×   40
 78.40
```

40 United States dollars equal 78.40 Barbados dollars.

Change 46 Barbados dollars to U.S. currency.

```
           23.469  ≈  23.47
1.96 ) 46.00 000
        39 2
        680
        588
         920
         784
        1360
        1176
         1840
         1764
```

46 Barbados dollars equal $23.47 in United States currency.

EXERCISE A.   Use the conversion chart on page 158 to make these currency conversions. Round any remainders to two decimal places.

1)   Change 43 United States dollars to Haitian currency.
2)   Change 36 Cayman Island dollars to United States currency.
3)   Change 30 East Carib dollars to United States currency.
4)   Change 52 United States dollars to Cuban currency.
5)   Change 85 United States dollars to Trinidad dollars.
6)   Change 78 Jamaican dollars to United States currency.
7)   Change $48.50 in United States currency to pesos.
8)   Change 75 gourdes to United States currency.

9) Change $46.76 in Bermudan currency to United States currency.

10) Change $8.52 in Cayman Island currency to United States currency.

11) Change $35.48 in United States currency to Barbados currency.

12) Change 52 Cuban pesos to United States currency.

13) Change 14 gourdes and 75 centimes to United States currency.

14) Change $42.56 in to United States currency to West Indies currency.

CRUISE RATES

You can purchase a packaged tour from a travel agent. This offers the air flight and the sea cruise for one basic price. The price that you pay depends on the city from which you fly and the deck your cabin is on.

Decks	Cruise Only Rates per Person	Flight/Cruise Package Rates			
		New York	Washington	Detroit	St. Louis
Errata	975.59	1160.02	1170.48	1210.62	1240.32
Clio	1005.48	1189.91	1200.37	1240.51	1270.21
Pollyp	1160.56	1344.99	1355.45	1395.59	1425.29
Thalia	1390.73	1575.16	1585.62	1625.76	1655.46
Child Under 12	250.45	434.88	446.34	485.48	515.18

Single Occupant Pays 1.5 Times the Cruise-Only Rate.

All rates are for one person and are for double occupancy.

EXERCISE A.   Using the chart on page 160, find the total cost.

Example:

If two people fly from Detroit and stay on the Clio deck, they will pay 2 × $1240.51, or $2481.02.

1)   Mr. and Mrs. Cardoza have a cabin on the Thalia deck. What is the cost of their trip if they fly from New York?

2)   Agatha and Albert Christie are taking their eight-year-old grandson on a cruise. They are leaving from St. Louis and are staying on the Errata deck. What is the total cost of their trip?

3)   The plane fare is the difference between the cruise-only rate and the flight/cruise rate. What is the plane fare from Washington?

4)   What is the plane fare from New York?

5)   Greg wants to fly from Detroit and stay in a cabin by himself on the Pollyp deck. How much will this trip cost? Do not forget about his plane fare.

Find the answers.

1) 48.6 - 5.324
2) 4.023 × 0.93
3) 9.048 ÷ 2.6
4) 36.83 + 9.284 + 52

Answer these word problems.

5) Tom drove to the beach for the day. When he left the house, his odometer read 16832 5. When he arrived at the beach, it read 16909 4. How far is it to the beach?

6) While driving, Mike saw a sign that read "Portland-187 miles."

Mike looked at his odometer and saw that it read 37042 5.

What will Mike's odometer read when he gets to Portland?

7) Find the total cost of 12.2 gallons of gasoline at $1.50 per gallon.

8) Will rented a mid-sized car for 4 days. He paid $16.95 per day plus 18¢ per mile. How much did Will pay if he drove the car 482 miles?

9) One U.S. dollar equals .85 Cayman Island dollars. What is 40 U.S. dollars in Cayman Island currency?

10) One U.S. dollar equals 1.79 Jamaican dollars. What is 62 Jamaican dollars in U.S. currency? Round to two decimal places.

11) How much would 11.5 gallons of gasoline cost at $1.75 per gallon?

12) Bob rented a compact car for $13.95 per day plus 16¢ per mile. Bob drove 382 miles in two days. How much did he pay?

Find the gas mileage.

Reading When Tank Was Filled	Gallons of Gas Bought	Reading at Second Filling	Gas Mileage
13) 48537.2	9.3	48835.8	___
14) 10736.5	5.8	10872.8	___

Use this road map to answer the questions below.

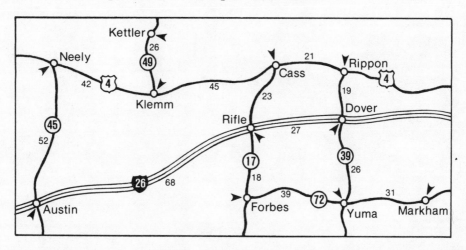

15) How far will you drive if you go from Dover to Klemm along ③⑨ and ④?

16) This trip took 1.7 hours. What was your average rate of speed?

17) You drove from Austin to Cass along ④⑤ and ④ How far did you drive?

18) You used 5.2 gallons of gas to make this trip. What is your gas mileage rounded to one decimal place?

19) You drove from Yuma to Cass along ⑦② and ①⑦. How far did you drive?

20) How much shorter would the trip have been if you had driven along ③⑨ and ④?

CHAPTER 11

WATCHING THE CLOCK

So much of our lives is controlled by time that we need to be able to tell time from a clock. Time is expressed using a colon. A time written as 7:42 is read "seven forty-two." The hour is given first. The number of minutes after the hour is given next. When reading the minutes, remember that each numbered space stands for five minutes. Each little space between the numbers stands for one minute.

Example:

What time is shown on each of these clocks?

4:33

2:17

1:52

EXERCISE A.   Write the time shown on each clock. Be sure to use a colon between the hour and minutes.

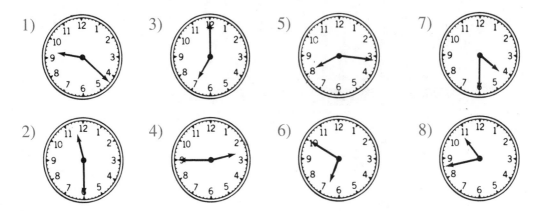

1)   3)   5)   7)

2)   4)   6)   8)

ELAPSED TIME

Elapsed time is the amount of time that has passed from one time to another. We find the amount of elapsed time by subtracting the earlier time from the later time. The later time is written on the top of a subtraction problem. If you must *rename*, remember that one hour is the same as sixty minutes.

Examples:
     How much time has elapsed from the time shown on Clock A to the time shown on Clock B?

1)   Clock A

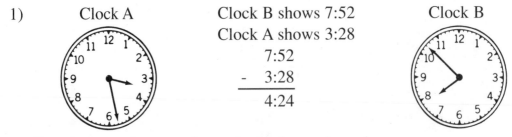

Clock B shows 7:52
Clock A shows 3:28

$$\begin{array}{r} 7:52 \\ - \quad 3:28 \\ \hline 4:24 \end{array}$$

Clock B

Four hours and twenty-four minutes have elapsed.

2)   Clock A   Clock B shows 7:21   Clock B

   Clock A shows 2:42

$$7:21 \leftarrow \text{Rename} \rightarrow 6:81$$
$$\underline{-\ 2:42} \quad \begin{array}{c}\text{1 hour}\\ \text{to 60}\\ \text{minutes}\end{array} \quad \underline{-\ 2:42}$$
$$4:39$$

Four hours and thirty-nine minutes have elapsed.

3)   Clock A   Clock B shows 4:33   Clock B

       Clock A shows 11:26

$$4:33 \leftarrow \text{Add} \rightarrow 16:33$$
$$\underline{-\ 11:26} \quad \text{12 hours} \quad \underline{-\ 11:26}$$
$$5:07$$

Five hours and seven minutes have elapsed.

EXERCISE A.   Subtract to find how much time has elapsed from the time shown on Clock A to the time shown on Clock B.

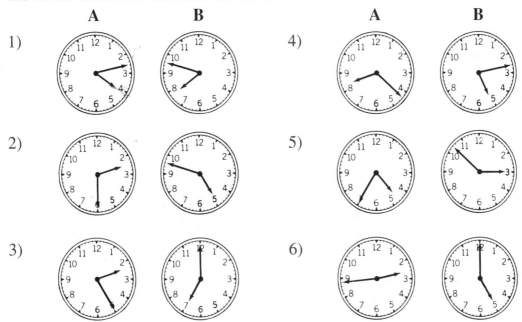

EXERCISE B.   Subtract to find the amount of time that has elapsed.

1)   From 3:46 to 7:58
2)   From 3:45 to 7:26
3)   From 5:18 to 7:25
4)   From 6:21 to 11:54
5)   From 3:59 to 4:16
6)   From 3:37 to 10:21
7)   From 1:45 to 11:26
8)   From 11:26 to 1:45
9)   From 3:16 to 8:42
10)   From 3:46 to 1:18

11)   From 12:15 to 2:30
12)   From 5:36 to 12:52
13)   From 6:27 to 3:49
14)   From 4:17 to 7:30
15)   From 6:30 to 10:42
16)   From 4:56 to 1:23
17)   From 5:45 to 9:51
18)   From 1:21 to 8:25
19)   From 3:56 to 11:21
20)   From 2:48 to 1:00

EXERCISE C.   Solve these word problems. You will need to use the clock next to each problem.

1)   Jeff Mason is waiting for a bus that is scheduled to arrive at 11:45. How long must Jeff wait?

2)   Carlo Bell's favorite TV program, "Albuquerque," comes on at 9:00. How long must Carlo wait for his show?

3)   Ginny went to sleep at 10:42 last night. When she woke up this morning, she looked at the clock by her bed. How long did she sleep?

4)   Barry arrived at the dentist's office at 12:15 for his appointment. He looked at his watch when his name was finally called. How long had Barry been waiting?

5) Maria left the house at 9:23 and drove to Dewey Beach. She arrived at the beach and looked at her dashboard clock. How long had Maria been driving?

6) The umpire stopped the game because of rain at 7:23. When play was resumed, Georgia looked at her watch. How long was the game delayed?

In some situations you know what time it is now and how many hours and minutes until some future event. You want to know what the time will be at the time of the event. To do a problem like this, you would add the hours and minutes to the current time.

Example:

Tell what time it will be when the given amount of time elapses from the time shown on the clock.

1)

$$
\begin{array}{r}
5:14 \\
+\ 3:28 \\
\hline
8:42
\end{array}
$$

3 hours, 28 min.

The new time
will be 8:42.

2)

$$
\begin{array}{r}
2:42 \\
+\ 2:35 \\
\hline
4:77 \\
\text{or } 5:17
\end{array}
$$

2 hours, 35 min.

(60 of the minutes
make 1 hour.)
The new time
will be 5:17.

3)

$$
\begin{array}{r}
11:22 \\
+\ 3:18 \\
\hline
14:40 \\
\text{or } 2:40
\end{array}
$$

3 hours, 18 min.

The new time
will be 2:40.

EXERCISE D.   Add to find the time after the given amount of time has elapsed.

1)

3 hours, 18 min.

2)

1 hour, 13 min.

3)

5 hours, 38 min.

4)

2 hours, 19 min.

5)

1 hour, 35 min.

6)

3 hours, 29 min.

7)

4 hours, 18 min.

8)

1 hour, 12 min.

9)

3 hours, 19 min.

10)

6 hours, 9 min.

11)

5 hours, 43 min.

12)

2 hours, 18 min.

TELEVISION SCHEDULES

To use a TV schedule, you need to be able to do simple time calculations.

EXERCISE A.   Answer the questions about this TV program listing.

1) At what time does "American Story" come on?

2) On what channel can you watch "Country Music Videos"?

3) How long is "Exercises"?

4) How long does the 6:45 news last?

5) What time does "Bugs Bunny and Friends" come on? What stations carry this program?

6) How long is Bob Turk on?

7) What times does "Stock Quotes" come on?

8) How long does "Bob's Place" last?

9) Fred turned on his TV at 6:43. How much of Captain Kangaroo had he missed?

10) At what times does Channel 7 broadcast news come on?

11) Willie woke up at 8:17. How many more minutes is the Mighty Mouse show on?

12) Jim turned on the TV at 6:42. How long did he wait for the "Casper" show to come on?

MORNING

Time				Program
5:20	4			Exercises
5:35	4			Aerobics
5:50	45			News
5:55	20			Bob's Place
6:00	2			News
	13			Morning Stretch
	45			Stock Quotes
	7			ABC News
	8			Early Today
	20			Pat's Recipe
6:05	4			Bob Turk
6:15	7			News
6:30	2	4		Early Today
	11			Learning To Do
	13			News
	45			Pat's Recipe
	7	47		ABC News
	8			Country Music Videos
	9			Captain Kangaroo
6:45	67	22		A.M. Weather
	7			News
7:00	2	4	8	Today
	11	9	16	Morning News
	13	7	47	Morning America
	45			Three Stooges
	67	22		American Story
	5			Stock Quotes
	20	9		Bugs Bunny & Friends
7:30	45			Little Rascals
	67	22		Sesame Street
	5			Great Space Coaster
	20			Woody Woodpecker
8:00	45			The Flintstones
	5			Porky Pig
	20			Mighty Mouse
8:30	45			Great Space Coaster
	67	22		Mister Rogers
	20			Casper
	26			MacNeil-Lehrer Hour

PARKING METERS

When you park your car, you may use a *metered parking space*. You will look at your watch, decide how long you need to run your errands, and then decide what time you must return to avoid getting a parking ticket. Once you know how much time you will be away from your car, put the required amount of money into the meter.

Example:

Tom put 35¢ in the parking meter at 2:43. By what time must he return?

35¢ for $1\frac{1}{2}$ + $\frac{1}{2}$ hour = 2 hours

$$\begin{array}{r} 2:43 \\ + \ 2:00 \\ \hline 4:43 \end{array}$$

Tom must return by 4:43.

Parking Rates
$1\frac{1}{2}$ hour for 25¢
$\frac{1}{2}$ hour for 10¢
$\frac{1}{4}$ hour for 5¢

EXERCISE A.   Answer these questions about parking meters. Use the parking rates above. Always use the most quarters that you can.

1) Lynn put 40¢ in the meter at 2:32. By what time must she return?

2) At 3:52 George put 15¢ in the meter. By what time must he return?

3) Donna put 45¢ in the meter at 11:42. By when must she return?

4) Ellie put 15¢ in the meter at 1:17. When must she return to her car?

5) Sam put 30¢ in the meter at 12:23. By what time must he return?

6) Anne parked her car at 10:48. She put 50¢ in the meter. By what time must Anne return?

7) Maggie will need twenty minutes to complete her errands. How much money should she put in the meter?

BUS SCHEDULES

Bus schedules indicate the leaving and arriving times for commercial buses. Understanding how these schedules work requires an understanding of elapsed time. Elapsed time is the amount of time it takes to complete a trip.

BUFFALO — ELMIRA — WILLIAMSPORT — SUNBURY
HARRISBURG—BALTIMORE—WASHINGTON

DOWN		7144		UP	
	EW 195	9-8-82		WE 196	
11 15	-----	Lv BUFFALO, N.Y. .... GL ..... Ar		-----	8 35
11 35	-----	Lv Buffalo Int'l Airport .... Ar *(start of same*		-----	8 15
f	-----	Lv Clarence .... Ar *schedule used)*		-----	f
12 35	-----	Lv Batavia .... Ar		-----	7 20
f	-----	Lv Pavilion .... Ar		-----	f
1 15	-----	Lv Mt. Morris .... Ar		-----	6 40
1 35	-----	Lv Dansville .... (257) .. Ar		-----	6 20
2 05	-----	Lv Hornell .... Ar		-----	5 50
2 45	-----	Lv Bath .... Ar		-----	5 10
f	-----	Lv Painted Post .... Ar		-----	f
3 15	-----	Ar Corning Lv		-----	4 40
3 30	-----	Lv Corning .... Ar		-----	4 25
3 55	-----	Ar ELMIRA, N.Y. .... GL ... Lv		-----	4 00
	2 25	Lv Binghamton, N.Y. .... CPB ... Ar		5 05	
	3 55	Ar Elmira, N.Y. .... (7143) ... Lv		3 30	
	4 30	Lv▲ELMIRA, N.Y. .... CPB ... Ar		3 30	
-----	f	Millerton, Pa.		f	-----
-----	hs	Tioga		hs	-----
-----	5 25	**Mansfield, Pa.**		2 30	-----
-----	f	Covington		f	-----
-----	5 35	▲Blossburg		2 15	-----
-----	f	Liberty		f	-----
-----	f	Trout Run		f	-----
	6 40	Ar▲**Williamsport, Pa.** ..... CPB ... Lv		1 20	
9 00		Lv Williamsport, Pa. .... TWI ... Ar			1 20
9 35		Ar Lock Haven, Pa. ..... (7866) ... Lv			12 35
10 25		Ar State College, Pa. Lv			11 35
-----	6 55	Lv▲**Williamsport, Pa.** ..... CPB ... Ar		12 55	-----
-----	f	Allenwood		f	-----
-----	7 35	▲**Lewisburg**		12 15	-----
-----	7 55	Ar▲**SUNBURY, PA.** .... CPB ... Lv		11 55	-----
-----	8 00	Lv SUNBURY, PA. .... GL ... Ar		11 50	-----
-----	9 20	Ar Harrisburg, Pa. Lv		10 30	-----
-----	10 15	Ar York, Pa. .... (265) ... Lv		9 10	-----
-----	11 25	Ar Baltimore, Md. Lv		8 00	-----
-----	12 20	Ar WASHINGTON, D.C. ...... GL ... Lv		6 50	-----

Bus schedules are really two schedules in one. The first is on the left, reading down. Bus 195 leaves Elmira at 4:30 and arrives in Williamsport at 6:40.

The second schedule is on the right, reading up. Bus 196 leaves Williamsport at 1:20 and arrives in Elmira at 3:30.

Here are some symbols that are used on a bus schedule:

Lv = leaves
Ar = arrives
f   = flag stop
hs = highway stop

Example:

How long does it take to ride the bus from Mansfield, PA, to Lewisburg, PA? Mansfield is above Lewisburg, so we use the left schedule reading down.

$$\begin{array}{r} 7:35 \\ - \ 5:25 \\ \hline 2:10 \end{array}$$

The bus ride takes 2 hours and 10 minutes.

EXERCISE A.   Answer these questions. Use the bus schedule on page 173.

1) It is now 12:45. How long will it be before the bus for Elmira leaves Dansville, NY?

2) It is now 5:23. How long will it be before the bus for Buffalo leaves Washington, D.C.?

3) John is riding the bus from Trout Run, PA to Batavia, NY. How long will the bus ride last?

4) Frank lives in Lewisburg. It takes Frank 20 minutes to walk to the bus station. What time must he leave his house if he is to catch the bus to York?

5) How long is the bus ride from:

   a) Bath to Blossburg?
   b) York to Elmira?
   c) Corning to Batavia?
   d) Hornell to Williamsport?
   e) Elmira to Mt. Morris?
   f) Baltimore to Mansfield?

Calculator Practice 11

CALCULATOR EXERCISE. Convert the following units of time. Use your calculator and the time chart.

1) 5 years = ___ days
2) 13 days = ___ hours
3) 6 hours = ___ minutes
4) 23 hours = ___ minutes
5) 42 days = ___ hours
6) 17 minutes = ___ seconds

Time Chart		
1 year	=	365 days
1 day	=	24 hours
1 hour	=	60 minutes
1 minute	=	60 seconds

PARKING LOT RATES

Many airports have different parking lots. The lot you park on will determine how much you pay. Refer to the following rates when answering the problems.

AIRPORT PARKING RATES
Short Term Lot

Up to 1/2 hour	$1.50
31 min. to 1 hr. and 5 min.	$2.00
1 hr. and 6 min. to 1 1/2 hrs.	$2.50
1 1/2 hours to 2 hours	$3.00
2 hours to 3 hours	$4.00
3 hours to 4 hours	$5.00
4 hours to 5 hours	$6.00
5 hours to 24 hours	$10.00

General Lot

Up to 1 hour	$1.00
1 hour to 3 hours	$2.00
3 hours to 8 hours	$3.50
8 hours to 24 hours	$7.50

Valet Lot

1 day	$10.00
2 days	$15.00
3 days	$18.00
Each additional day	$5.00

Example:

Gwen parked her car at 2:47 pm. She was meeting some friends at the airport. The flight was delayed. She left the lot at 4:26 pm. How much did Gwen pay for parking?

$$
\begin{array}{r}
4:26 \\
-2:47 \\
\hline
1:39
\end{array} \quad = \quad 1 \text{ hour } 39 \text{ minutes}
$$

The price Gwen paid for parking:

...if she was on the short term lot........................$ 3.00
...if she was on the general lot ....$ 2.00
...if she was on the valet lot $10.00

EXERCISE A.   Answer these questions about parking at the airport.

1) Greg parked on the general lot from 12:48 pm to 1:19 pm. How much did he pay?

2) Diane is making a short business trip. She parked her car at 7:23. She plans to return at 4:50. Which lot should she use to pay the least amount of parking fees?

3) How much will Diane pay?

4) Cindy and Jerry are going to Seattle for 6 days. How much will they pay for parking on the valet lot while they are gone?

5) How much would you pay for parking:
   a) from 8:52 pm to 10:03 pm on the short term lot?
   b) from 12:34 pm to 1:17 pm on the general lot?
   c) from 9:23 am to 12:31 pm on the general lot?

Computer Practice 11

Have you ever wondered how old you are in hours, minutes, or seconds? Use this program and be surprised at the results. (See Appendix for more information.)

COMPUTER EXERCISE. Run the following program. Type in your own age in years.

```
10    PRINT   "CONVERTING YEARS TO DAYS, HOURS, MINUTES,
               AND SECONDS"
20    INPUT   "YOUR AGE IN YEARS ";Y
30    D = Y * 365
40    H = D * 24
50    M = H * 60
60    S = M * 60
70    PRINT Y;" YEARS"
80    PRINT D;" DAYS"
90    PRINT H;" HOURS"
100   PRINT M;" MINUTES"
110   PRINT S;" SECONDS"
120   END
```

CHAPTER TEST

11

Answer these questions.

1) What time is it on this clock?

2) How much time has elapsed from Clock A to Clock B?

3) The baseball game begins at 12:15 pm. It is now 12:08 pm. How long will it be until the game starts?

4) How much time elapses from 11:23 am to 2:45 pm?

5) What time will it be when it is 3 hours and 25 minutes later than the time shown on this clock?

6) The sign on the parking meter says, "Half-hour for 10¢." You put 30¢ in the meter at 11:42 am. By what time must you return?

7) How long is the Channel 45's news program?

5:20	4	Exercises
5:35	4	Aerobics
5:50	45	News
5:55	20	Bob's Place
6:00	2	News
	13	Morning Stretch
	45	Stock Quotes
	5	Panorama
	7	ABC News
	8	Early Today

8) Oswald's Parking Lot charges $1.25 for the first hour and 50¢ for each half-hour after that. How much will you pay at Oswald's from 7:52 am to 12:15 pm?

9) How long is the bus ride from Sunbury, PA to Washington, D.C.? Use the schedule on page 173.

10) How long is the bus ride from Corning, NY to Batavia, NY?

CHAPTER 12

BASEBALL STATISTICS

Baseball has been described as a small island of activity played in an ocean of *statistics*. These statistics include the team standings, the players' batting averages and fielding percentages, and the pitcher's earned run average. Player statistics are listed on the back of each baseball card. Baseball statistics can also be found in the sports section of the daily newspaper.

Almost all statistics are found by making a ratio of successes to attempts. This ratio is expressed as a decimal rounded to three places. The mathematical skill needed is the ability to divide a small number by a larger number and to express the answer as a decimal.

For example, if Sandy Davis gets five hits out of her eleven times at bat, we can find her batting average.

5 hits out of eleven times at bat. $$\frac{5}{11} = \frac{\text{Number of hits}}{\text{Number of times at bat}}$$

Express 5 out of 11, or $\dfrac{5}{11}$, as a decimal rounded to three places.

$$
\begin{array}{r}
.4545 \approx .455 \\
11\,)\overline{5.0000} \\
44 \\
\overline{60} \\
55 \\
\overline{50} \\
44 \\
\overline{60} \\
55 \\
\overline{}
\end{array}
$$

Divide to four places and round to three.

EXERCISE A.   Change each fraction to a decimal rounded to three places.

1) $\dfrac{4}{13}$ =

2) $\dfrac{7}{8}$ =

3) $\dfrac{4}{9}$ =

4) $\dfrac{7}{12}$ =

5) $\dfrac{3}{4}$ =

6) $\dfrac{4}{5}$ =

7) $\dfrac{3}{8}$ =

8) $\dfrac{2}{15}$ =

BATTING AVERAGES

A baseball player's batting average is a measure of how well he hits. The higher the batting average, the better the player hits. A batting average is written as a decimal rounded to three places. A player's batting average is found by dividing the number of hits by the number of times at bat the player has had. Walks and sacrifice outs do not count as official times at bat.

Example:
   If a player has 24 hits for 62 at bats, what is his batting average?

Batting average $= \dfrac{\text{Number of hits}}{\text{Number of times at bat}} = \dfrac{5}{12}$

$$\begin{array}{r} .3870 \approx .387 \\ 62 \overline{)\ 24.0000} \\ \underline{186} \\ 540 \\ \underline{496} \\ 440 \\ \underline{434} \\ 60 \end{array}$$

EXERCISE A.   Find the batting average for each player.

1)   Ymato Ma
    45 at bats
    18 hits

2)   Gail Wills
    32 at bats
    12 hits

3)   Mike Speer
    90 at bats
    26 hits

4)   Sol Lausch
    51 at bats
    15 hits

5)   Gil French
    43 at bats
    25 hits

6)   Walt Jones
    73 at bats
    37 hits

7)   Gwen Smith
    28 at bats
    9 hits

8)   Ben Cardin
    63 at bats
    35 hits

9)   Vic Salski
    29 at bats
    15 hits

10)   Jake Shane
    51 at bats
    20 hits

11)   Tom Foster
    28 at bats
    10 hits

12)   Robin Jay
    22 at bats
    6 hits

SLUGGING PERCENTAGES

Two baseball players may have the same batting average, but the first player may hit the ball farther, resulting in his getting to more bases — either a double, triple, or home run. The player who hits the ball a shorter distance may only make it to first base — a single. A baseball statistic that fans use to measure how well a player bats is the slugging percentage, given as a decimal rounded to three places.

For example, what is this player's slugging percentage? Remember, walks and sacrifices don't count.

$$\text{Slugging Percentage} \quad = \quad \frac{\text{Total Bases}}{\text{Official at Bats}}$$

Home runs count as four bases, triples count as three bases, and so on.

3	home runs →	12	→	3	
2	triples →	6	→	2	
10	doubles →	20	→	10	
15	singles →	+ 15	→	15	
9	walks	53 Bases		+ 32	
32	outs			62	At Bats
7	sacrifices				

```
         .8548   ≈   .855
     62 ) 53.0000
         49 6
          3 40
          3 10
           300
           248
           520
           496
            24
```

EXERCISE A.   Find each player's slugging percentage. Remember that walks and sacrifices do not count as official at bats.

1)   Bill Light
    1 home run
    4 triples
    6 doubles
    16 singles
    5 walks
    21 outs
    7 sacrifices

2)   Skip Carr
    4 home runs
    12 triples
    6 doubles
    11 singles
    8 walks
    12 outs
    15 sacrifices

3)   George Gill
    0 home runs
    1 triple
    4 doubles
    15 singles
    3 walks
    21 outs
    3 sacrifices

4)   Riva Lewis
    5 home runs
    1 triple
    11 doubles
    21 singles
    4 walks
    20 outs
    9 sacrifices

5)   Iona Williams
    2 home runs
    6 triples
    5 doubles
    13 singles
    18 walks
    32 outs
    6 sacrifices

6)   Joe Leake
    3 home runs
    0 triples
    2 doubles
    8 singles
    10 walks
    18 outs
    8 sacrifices

FRACTIONS AS PERCENTS

A fraction may be written as a percent by following these steps:

Step 1:   Divide the denominator into the numerator.
Step 2:   Divide to four decimal places.
Step 3:   Round to three decimal places.
Step 4:   Multiply your rounded quotient by 100.

An easy way to perform the last step is to move the decimal point two places to the right.

Examples:

Rewrite $\frac{8}{11}$ as a decimal. Then, convert the decimal to a percent.

$$.7272 \quad \approx \quad .727 \quad = \quad 72.7\%$$

```
      .7272
 11 ) 8.0000
      7 7
       30
       22
        80
        77
        30
```

Rewrite $\frac{7}{8}$ as a decimal. Then, convert the decimal to a percent.

$$.875 \quad = \quad 87.5\%$$

```
     .875
 8 ) 7.000
     6 4
      60
      56
      40
      40
       0
```

Some quotients will terminate before the fourth decimal place.

EXERCISE A.   Rewrite these fractions as percents. If the division does not divide evenly, round to three decimal places.

1) $\dfrac{4}{7}$ 5) $\dfrac{4}{11}$ 9) $\dfrac{4}{5}$ 13) $\dfrac{7}{15}$

2) $\dfrac{7}{12}$ 6) $\dfrac{3}{4}$ 10) $\dfrac{5}{7}$ 14) $\dfrac{5}{9}$

3) $\dfrac{3}{8}$ 7) $\dfrac{5}{6}$ 11) $\dfrac{6}{13}$ 15) $\dfrac{2}{9}$

4) $\dfrac{8}{9}$ 8) $\dfrac{2}{3}$ 12) $\dfrac{1}{8}$ 16) $\dfrac{5}{8}$

BASERUNNING AVERAGES

After a player gets on base, he may try to steal the next base. This adds to the excitement of the game and advances the base runner to scoring position. How successful a base runner is at stealing bases is measured by his *baserunning average*. The baserunning average is found by dividing the number of bases stolen by the number of attempts. It is given as a *percent*. The percent is found by multiplying the decimal by 100.

For example, Bobby Kemp stole 15 bases and was *putout* 27 times while attempting to steal. What is Bobby's baserunning average?

$$\text{Baserunning Average} \;=\; \frac{\text{Bases Stolen}}{\text{Attempted Steals}}$$

$(15 + 27 = 42)$

$$\text{Baserunning Average} = \frac{15}{42}$$

$$.3571 \approx .357 = 35.7\% \quad \leftarrow \text{Baserunning Average}$$

$$
\begin{array}{r}
42 \overline{)15.0000} \\
12\,6 \\
\hline
240 \\
210 \\
\hline
300 \\
294 \\
\hline
60
\end{array}
$$

EXERCISE A.   Find the baserunning average for each record.

1) 16 steals
    8 putouts

2) 24 steals
    30 putouts

3) 45 steals
    18 putouts

4) 21 steals
    12 putouts

5) 36 steals
    14 putouts

6) 18 steals
    7 putouts

7) 30 steals
    16 putouts

8) 19 steals
    7 putouts

9) 41 steals
    28 putouts

10) 16 steals
     6 putouts

11) 14 steals
     18 putouts

12) 38 steals
     16 putouts

13) 30 steals
     7 putouts

14) 51 steals
     21 putouts

15) 46 steals
     30 putouts

FIELDING PERCENTAGE

The effectiveness of a fielder is measured with the *fielding percentage*. It is found by dividing the total number of chances that the fielder had to make a play into the number of *assists* plus the number of putouts.

A player's fielding percentage is given as a decimal rounded to three places. The total chances are: assists + putouts + errors.

For example, during one game, Mario Martinez made 16 assists and 8 putouts while committing 2 errors. What was Mario's fielding percentage?

Fielding Percentage $= \dfrac{\text{Assists + Putouts}}{\text{Total Chances}}$

Fielding Percentage $= \dfrac{16 + 8}{16 + 8 + 2} = \dfrac{24}{26}$

$$
\begin{array}{r}
.9230 \\
26 \overline{)\ 24.0000} \\
\underline{23\ 4} \\
60 \\
\underline{52} \\
80 \\
\underline{78} \\
20
\end{array}
$$

$\approx$ .923   ← Fielding percentage

EXERCISE A.   Express each player's fielding percentage as a decimal rounded to three places.

1)   J. J. John
      8 assists
      7 putouts
      2 errors

2)   Chris Sneed
      8 assists
      13 putouts
      1 error

3)   Greg Kohn
      9 assists
      17 putouts
      4 errors

4)   Elva Ellis
      8 assists
      15 putouts
      0 errors

5)   John Gaines
      16 assists
      23 putouts
      3 errors

6)   Ty Herr
      12 assists
      6 putouts
      4 errors

7)   Beth Wells
      5 assists
      2 putouts
      1 error

8)   Craig Rolf
      11 assists
      0 putouts
      3 errors

9)   Jay Baden
      14 assists
      1 putout
      0 errors

EARNED RUN AVERAGE

The most important statistic to a pitcher is his *earned run average*. The ERA is a measure of how many runs a pitcher allows in a game. It is found by multiplying the number of runs that the pitcher has allowed by 9 and then dividing by the number of innings that the pitcher has pitched. Any parts of an inning pitched are rounded off to the nearest whole number. $21\frac{1}{3}$ innings becomes 21 innings. $21\frac{2}{3}$ innings becomes 22 innings.

$$\text{Earned Run Average} \quad = \quad \frac{\text{Earned Runs} \times 9}{\text{Innings Pitched}}$$

For example, Cara Klemens allowed 6 runs in 23 innings. What is her earned run average?

$$\text{Earned Run Average} \quad = \quad \frac{6 \times 9}{23} \quad = \quad \frac{54}{23}$$

$$
\begin{array}{r}
2.347 \\
23 \overline{\smash{)}54.000} \\
46 \\
\hline
8\,0 \\
6\,9 \\
\hline
110 \\
92 \\
\hline
180 \\
161 \\
\hline
19
\end{array}
$$

$\approx \quad 2.35 \qquad \leftarrow$ Earned run average

EXERCISE A.   Find each pitcher's earned run average. Express the ERA as a decimal rounded to two places.

1)   Lee Gonzalez

16 innings

3 earned runs

4)   Bob Gold

$17\frac{2}{3}$ innings

6 earned runs

7)   Tom Provo

14 innings

5 earned runs

2)   Gwen Statham

24 innings

2 earned runs

5)   Cranston Cross

$23\frac{1}{3}$ innings

5 earned runs

8)   Harrison Kirk

8 innings

3 earned runs

3)   Larry McCoy

18 innings

2 earned runs

6)   Peter Connally

$21\frac{1}{3}$ innings

4 earned runs

9)   Lisa Warlaw

28 innings

2 earned runs

WON-LOST PERCENTAGE

The most important statistic for a team is the team's *won-lost percentage*. The team with the largest won-lost percentage is in first place. The won-lost percentage is written as a decimal rounded to three places. It is found by dividing the number of team wins by the number of games that team has played.

$$\text{Won-Lost Percentage} \quad = \quad \frac{\text{Number of Wins}}{\text{Games Played}}$$

For example, the Mets have won 14 games and lost 18 games. What is their won-lost percentage?

$$\text{Won-Lost Percentage} \quad = \quad \frac{14}{14 + 18} \quad = \quad \frac{14}{32}$$

```
        .4375    ≈    .438      ← Won-lost percentage
  32 ) 14.0000
       12 8
        1 20
          96
         240
         224
         160
         160
```

EXERCISE A. Find each team's won-lost percentage. Then, list the teams in order of their standing. The team with the largest won-lost percentage in each division is in first place. The other teams follow in the order of their won-lost percentages.

American League
Eastern Division

Team	Won	Lost
Milwaukee	42	43
Baltimore	50	37
Boston	39	48
Detroit	55	32
New York	44	41
Cleveland	57	30
Toronto	43	44

Western Division

Team	Won	Lost
Kansas City	24	63
California	52	35
Chicago	28	59
Seattle	30	56
Oakland	48	37
Texas	39	47
Minnesota	54	33

National League
Eastern Division

Team	Won	Lost
St. Louis	48	38
Philadelphia	49	37
Montreal	27	58
Pittsburgh	50	36
Chicago	34	53
New York	53	33

Western Division

Team	Won	Lost
Los Angeles	50	37
Atlanta	45	43
San Francisco	25	62
San Diego	54	34
Houston	47	40
Cincinnati	38	49

Calculator Practice 12

You may use a calculator to convert fractions to decimals than to percents.

Example:

Express $\frac{7}{12}$ as a percent.

Step 1: Divide the numerator by the denominator.
$7 \div 12 = .5833333$

Step 2: Round the answer to the nearest thousandth.
$.5833333 \approx .583$

Step 3: Move the decimal point two places to the right. Write the answer as a percent.
$.583 = 58.3\%$

CALCULATOR EXERCISE. Express these fractions as decimals, then as percents. Use a calculator.

1) $\frac{7}{8}$ 6) $\frac{4}{5}$ 11) $\frac{2}{3}$ 16) $\frac{1}{6}$

2) $\frac{5}{6}$ 7) $\frac{1}{7}$ 12) $\frac{9}{13}$ 17) $\frac{11}{16}$

3) $\frac{4}{12}$ 8) $\frac{2}{7}$ 13) $\frac{3}{17}$ 18) $\frac{2}{5}$

4) $\frac{9}{11}$ 9) $\frac{12}{13}$ 14) $\frac{5}{19}$ 19) $\frac{4}{9}$

5) $\frac{9}{10}$ 10) $\frac{5}{8}$ 15) $\frac{2}{21}$ 20) $\frac{3}{4}$

GAMES BACK

A statistic given with the won-lost percentage is the number of games that each team is back from first place. The number of *games back* from first place is found by comparing the wins and losses of each team with those of the first place team.

$$\text{Games Back} \quad = \quad \frac{\text{Difference of Wins} + \text{Differences of Losses}}{2}$$

Example:

Team	Won	Lost	Pct.	GB
California	23	14	.622	—
Texas	19	18	.514	?
Oakland	17	19	.472	?

$$\text{Texas—Games Back} \quad = \quad \frac{(23 - 19) + (18 - 14)}{2}$$

$$= \quad \frac{4 + 4}{2} \quad = \quad 4$$

$$\text{Oakland—Games Back} \quad = \quad \frac{(23 - 17) + (19 - 14)}{2}$$

$$= \quad \frac{6 + 5}{2} \quad = \quad 5\frac{1}{2}$$

EXERCISE A. For each division, compute the teams' won-lost percentage and the number of games back.

American League—*Eastern Division*

Team	Won	Lost	Pct.	GB
Milwaukee	37	10	?	—
Baltimore	34	12	?	?
Boston	33	14	?	?
Detroit	24	23	?	?
New York	20	27	?	?
Cleveland	12	40	?	?
Toronto	10	43	?	?

American League—*Western Division*

Team	Won	Lost	Pct.	GB
Kansas City	34	13	?	—
California	28	19	?	?
Chicago	23	20	?	?
Seattle	19	23	?	?
Oakland	18	25	?	?
Texas	17	26	?	?
Minnesota	16	30	?	?

National League—*Eastern Division*					National League—*Western Division*				
Team	Won	Lost	Pct.	GB	**Team**	Won	Lost	Pct.	GB
St. Louis	33	18	?	—	Los Angeles	33	13	?	—
Philadelphia	32	20	?	?	Atlanta	30	17	?	?
Montreal	29	28	?	?	San Francisco	27	20	?	?
Pittsburgh	22	27	?	?	San Diego	25	23	?	?
Chicago	21	28	?	?	Houston	18	29	?	?
New York	15	30	?	?	Cincinnati	11	42	?	?

Computer Practice 12

Use a computer to express fractions as percents. To stop the program, type "0" for the denominator. (See Appendix for more information.)

```
10    PRINT "TO EXPRESS A FRACTION AS A PERCENT"
20    INPUT "NUMERATOR = ";A
30    INPUT "DENOMINATOR = ";B
40    IF B = 0 THEN 80
50    X = INT (A/B * 1000 + .5)/10
60    PRINT X;" %"
70    GOTO 20
80    END
```

COMPUTER EXERCISE.   Check your answers to the calculator exercise on page 191.

Rename each fraction as a decimal rounded to three places.

1) $\dfrac{7}{8}$

2) $\dfrac{5}{13}$

Rename each fraction as a percent. Round to one decimal place.

3) $\dfrac{3}{7}$

4) $\dfrac{7}{12}$

Give the batting average for each player as a three place decimal.

5) Pat Pace/8 hits for 21 at bats

6) Jo Cox/15 hits for 38 at bats

Give the slugging percentage for each player as a three place decimal.

7) Henry Wolpert

1 home run	3 walks
2 triples	10 outs
4 doubles	8 sacrifices
8 singles	

8) Juan Cortez

0 home runs	6 walks
1 triple	9 outs
3 doubles	2 sacrifices
12 singles	

Give each baserunning average as a percent rounded to one decimal.

9) Hector Iliad stole 18 bases and was putout 13 times while attempting to steal.

10) Sam Smith stole 9 bases and was putout 14 times while attempting to steal.

Give each player's fielding percentage as a decimal rounded to three places.

11) Joe Shaw had 8 assists and 4 putouts. He made 2 errors.

12) Morris Corona had 7 assists and 9 putouts. He made 1 error.

Give each pitcher's ERA as a two place decimal.

13) Don Coleman pitched 14 innings and allowed 8 earned runs.

14) Marian Finney pitched 24 innings and allowed 8 earned runs.

For each team find the won-lost percentage and the number of games that the team trails the first place team.

15)

Team	Won	Lost	Pct.	GB
Texas	33	15	?	—
Kansas City	29	18	?	?
California	27	21	?	?

CHAPTER 13

USING PERCENT

As you use your hard-earned money, you frequently find that you need to use percents. When you buy something at a store, you might pay a sales tax on the purchase price. A sales tax is expressed as a percent. The item may be on sale for 20 percent off. You may have budgeted a percent of your income for this purchase. Can you afford the item?

Instead of buying something, you might decide to save your money in a savings account. The account will pay a rate of interest expressed as a percent.

There are three elements in any percent sentence: the rate, the base, and the percentage. The *rate* is the percent. The *base* is the whole amount. The *percentage* is the part, the number that you get when you take the percent of the base.

$$20\% \quad \text{of} \quad 40 \quad \text{is} \quad 8.$$

↑		↑		↑
Rate		Base		Percentage

Rate × Base = Percentage

Example:
   3% of 52 is ?

Step 1:   Change 3% to .03 by moving the decimal point 2 places to the left.
Step 2:   Multiply.

$$\begin{array}{rl} 52 & \text{Base} \\ \times \ \ .03 & \text{Rate} \\ \hline 1.56 & \text{Percentage} \end{array}$$

   3% of 52 is 1.56.

EXERCISE A.   Find the percentages.
   1)   20% of 53 is ____
   2)   33% of 18 is ____
   3)   13% of 7.5 is ____
   4)   25% of 38 is ____
   5)   28% of 100 is ____
   6)   29% of 35 is ____
   7)   6% of 30 is ____
   8)   9% of 365 is ____
   9)   .7% of 150 is ____
   10)   2.7% of 38 is ____

SALES TAX

   A state *sales tax* is collected for most sales. Although not all states have a sales tax, the majority do. This money is used by the state for such things as education, police protection, and keeping the highways in good condition. To compute a sales tax is to find a percentage.

   For example, Bill bought a school notebook for $5.85. There was a sales tax of 5%. What was the price of the notebook with the tax?

Step 1: Multiply the price by the rate of the tax.

$5.85   Original price
× .05   Rate of tax
$.2925   Tax
$.2925   ≈ .30 (State sales tax is always rounded up.)

Step 2: Add the tax to the original price.

$5.85   Original price
+ .30   Tax
$6.15   Total price including tax

EXERCISE A.   Find the sales tax and the total price including tax.

1) Repair book $12.95 with a 5% sales tax
2) Calculator $9.65 with a 5% sales tax
3) Mirror $55.60 with a 6% sales tax
4) Candy mints $2.20 with a 6% sales tax
5) Shirt $22.99 with a 5% sales tax
6) Shoes $55 with a 4% sales tax
7) Dictionary $9 with a 5% sales tax
8) Tie $6.50 with a 6% sales tax
9) Candy bar $.49 with a 5% sales tax
10) Baking dish $8.50 with a 7% sales tax
11) Napkins $.85 with a 6% sales tax
12) Bookshelf $39.95 with a 5% sales tax
13) Briefcase $21.20 with a 5% sales tax
14) Blanket $32.00 with a 6% sales tax
15) Picture frame $16 with a 4% sales tax
16) Car $7285.92 with a 5% sales tax
17) Surfboard $275 with a 5% sales tax
18) Lamp $29.99 with a 6% sales tax
19) Clock $12.35 with a 7% sales tax
20) Night stand $88 with a 5% sales tax
21) Notebook $6.95 with a 6% sales tax
22) Index cards $.59 with a 5% sales tax

DISCOUNT

Sales are often advertised in the form of *discounts*, such as "10% off." Knowing the exact amount of the discount is important for wise shoppers. To calculate a discount is to find a percentage.

For example, Jenny wanted a bike that originally cost $90. If she got a 25% discount, how much would the bike cost?

Step 1: Multiply the original price by the rate of discount.

$$
\begin{array}{r}
\$90.00 \\
\times \quad .25 \\
\hline
4\ 5000 \\
18\ 000 \\
\hline
\$22.5000
\end{array}
$$

    $90.00   Original price
×   .25   Rate of discount
4 5000
18 000
$22.5000   Discount

Step 2: Subtract the discount from the original price.

    $90.00   Original price
-   22.50   Discount
    $67.50   Sale price

With a 25% discount, the bike would cost $67.50.

Example:

Kristina picked out a winter coat with a price tag of $89.50. The coat was on sale at 15% off the marked price. How much of a discount will she get? What is the new sale price?

Step 1: Multiply.

    $89.50   Original price
×   .15   Rate of discount
4 4750
8 950
$13.4250 ≈ $13.43

Step 2: Subtract.

    $89.50   Original price
-   13.43   Discount
    $76.07   Sale price

EXERCISE A.   Find the discount and the new sale price for each.
1)   Radio $169.00 with a discount rate of 20%
2)   Calculator $14.20 with a discount rate of 10%
3)   Shirt $17.00 with a discount rate of 15%
4)   Shoes $32.50 with a discount rate of 20%
5)   Blouse $16.75 with a discount rate of 25%
6)   Handbag $10 with a discount rate of 10%
7)   Flashlight $3.95 with a discount rate of 10%
8)   Baseball $4.50 with a discount rate of 25%
9)   Television $289 with a discount rate of 30%
10)   Rug $175.92 with a discount rate of 10%
11)   Chair $109.68 with a discount rate of 15%
12)   Shovel $10.99 with a discount rate of 25%
13)   Notebook $6.25 with a discount rate of 20%
14)   Computer $349 with a discount rate of 15%
15)   Scarf $2.75 with a discount rate of 50%
16)   Bike $110.25 with a discount rate of 10%
17)   Skates $52.98 with a discount rate of 40%
18)   Cassette deck $48.95 with a discount rate of 12%
19)   Computer game $200 with a discount rate of 20%
20)   Typewriter $159 with a discount rate of 25%
21)   Lawn mower $289 with a discount rate of 15%
22)   Hammer $18.60 with a discount rate of 10%

PERSONAL SPENDING

One step in budget planning is to find out what percent of earnings is usually spent on certain items. You can find the percent, or rate, by dividing.

For example, Sandee earns $222 per week and spends $50 per week for food. What percent of her salary does she spend on food per week?

Rate × Base	=	Percentage
___% of $222	=	$50
___%	=	$50 ÷ $222

```
          .225
222 ) 50.000      ← Insert enough zeros to allow 3 decimal places.
      44 4
       5 60
       4 44
       1 160
       1 110
          50
```

To express a decimal as a percent, move the decimal point two places to the right.

.225 = 22.5%

Sandee spends 22.5% of her salary for food.

EXERCISE A.   Find the rate of earnings spent.

1)   Lee spends $50 of his income on apartment rent. If he earns $170 per week, what percent does he spend on rent?

2)   Lindy earns $65 per week and spends $18 on bus fare. What percent does she spend on bus fare?

3)   Laurie needs $7 each week for lunch. If she earns $18 per week, what percent is spent for lunch?

4)   Marnie earned $170 last week and spent $40 for food. What percent was spent for food?

5)   Nicholas earned $56 last week and spent $45 for food. What percent was spent for food?

6)   Cara earned $18 last week and spent $15 on bus fare. What percent was spent on bus fare?

7)   Jeff earned $52 last week and spent $25 on clothes. What percent was spent on clothes?

8)   Ben earned $28 last week. He spent $5 on bus fare and $5 on lunches. What percent was spent on bus fare? What percent was spent on lunches?

9) Rita earned $85 last week. She spent $10 for bus fare and $8 on lunches. What percent was spent on bus fare? What percent was spent on lunches?

10) Malcolm earned $262 last week. He spent $16 last week for bus fare and $50 for a car payment. What percent was spent on bus fare? What percent was spent on the car payment?

11) Jesse earned $350 last week. He spent $15 on clothes and $75 for rent. What percent was spent on clothes? What percent was spent on rent?

12) Luis earned $170 last week. He spent $25 on books and $35 on his gas bill. What percent was spent on books? What percent was spent on the gas bill?

13) Erica earned $275. She spent $55 on her phone bill and $51 on a birthday party for a friend. What percent was spent on her phone bill? What percent was spent on the birthday party?

PERSONAL SAVINGS

If you know the rate of earnings saved and the percentage of earnings saved, you can find the total earnings by dividing.

For example, Donnell is saving 20% of his earnings for college. If he saves $17 per week, how much does he earn per week?

Rate × Base = Percentage
20% × ___ = $17
        ___ = $17 ÷ .20   Because 20% is .20.

```
        $  85.
  .20 )$17.00
         16 0
          1 00
          1 00
```

Base = $85. Donnell earns $85 per week.

Example:

Lionel saves 15% of his weekly wages. If he saves $13.80 per week, what are his weekly wages?

Rate $\times$ Base $=$ Percentage

15% $\times$ ___ $=$ $13.80

___ $=$ $13.80 \div .15

$$
\begin{array}{r}
\$92. \\
.15\,\overline{)\$13.80} \\
13\ 5 \\
\hline
30 \\
30 \\
\hline
\end{array}
$$

Base = $92. Lionel earns $92 per week.

EXERCISE A.   Find the earnings.

1)   Abbott is saving 30% of his weekly salary for a car. If he saves $24.60 per week, how much does he earn per week?

2)   Wayne deposits 25% of his weekly earnings in a savings account. If he deposits $19.50 weekly, how much does he earn?

3)   Rachel saves $32.90 per week from her part-time babysitting job. If she saves 35% of her earnings, how much does she earn?

4)   Bo wants to save 25% of his weekly income for school. How much will he have to make to save $11.75 per week?

EXERCISE B. Find the weekly earnings.

1) 20% saved
Saved $80
Earned ____

2) 25% saved
Saved $22.50
Earned ____

3) 20% saved
Saved $13
Earned ____

4) 30% saved
Saved $16.20
Earned ____

5) 35% saved
Saved $13.30
Earned ____

6) 22% saved
Saved $12.10
Earned ____

7) 15% saved
Saved $12.15
Earned ____

8) 40% saved
Saved $42
Earned ____

9) 10% saved
Saved $2.60
Earned ____

10) 12% saved
Saved $18
Earned ____

USING CIRCLE GRAPHS

Budgets are often shown with a *circle graph*. Each section of the graph represents a different kind of expense. You can clearly see what rate of total earnings is spent for each purpose.

Example:

Construct a circle graph to show Jim's budget.

Jim's Budget
Rent, 25%
Car, 10%
Savings, 30%
Other, 35%

Follow these steps:

Step 1: Construct a circle. Mark the center.

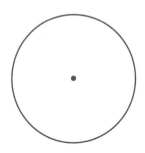

Step 2: There are 360° in a circle. Find the number of degrees needed for each item by multiplying the percent by 360°.

.25	×	360°	=	90°	**Rent**
.10	×	360°	=	36°	**Car**
.30	×	360°	=	108°	**Savings**
.35	×	360°	=	126°	**Other**

Step 3: Construct a *radius* and use a *protractor* to measure and draw each portion.

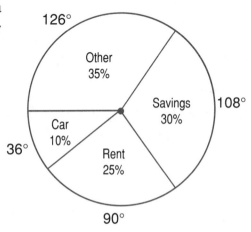

EXERCISE A.   Construct a circle graph for each budget. Round degrees to the nearest whole number.

1) Rent 25%
   Food 15%
   Car 15%
   Other 45%

2) Rent 30%
   Food 25%
   Car 10%
   Other 35%

3) Rent 20%
   Clothing 15%
   Savings 5%
   Other 60%

4) Entertainment 14%
   Housing 26%
   Savings 10%
   Other 50%

5) Transportation 15%
   Savings 20%
   Food 35%
   Housing 20%
   Clothing 10%

6) Entertainment 5%
   Housing 20%
   Food 30%
   Clothing 15%
   Other 30%

7) Rent 25%
   Food 22%
   Clothing 18%
   Other 35%

8) Savings 15%
   Food 17%
   Clothing 13%
   Other 55%

9) Food 25%
   Housing 30%
   Car 10%
   Clothing 15%
   Other 20%

10) Mortgage 25%
    Clothing 10%
    Car 15%
    Savings 35%
    Other 15%

11) Transportation 20%
    Food 25%
    Car 20%
    Savings 15%
    Clothing 20%

12) Entertainment 5%
    Housing 25%
    Food 25%
    Savings 10%
    Other 35%

Calculator Practice 13

You may use your calculator to find discounts.

Example:

Find the discount of 20% on $55.88.

Step 1: Multiply the price by the discount rate.

$55.88 × .20 = $11.176

Step 2: Round your answer to the nearest cent.

$11.176 ≈ $11.18

CALCULATOR EXERCISE. Use your calculator to find the discounts.

1) $25 at 25%
2) $13.50 at 22%
3) $125.52 at 32%
4) $18.95 at 10%
5) $120 at 35%
6) $1.95 at 20%
7) $32.89 at 15%
8) $103.75 at 60%

Computer Practice 13

This computer program will find the percentage of a number. (See Appendix for more information.)

```
10   PRINT "FINDING THE PERCENTAGE OF A NUMBER"
20   PRINT "WHAT IS THE NUMBER?"
30   INPUT A
40   PRINT "TYPE THE RATE AS A DECIMAL."
50   INPUT B
60   IF A = 0 THEN 90
70   PRINT A * B
80   GOTO 20
90   END
```

To stop the program, type 0 for the number.

COMPUTER EXERCISE.   Use your computer to find the percentages.

1)   26% of 28.35
2)   2.6% of 41031
3)   4.9% of 53
4)   175% of 26.3
5)   33% of 26309
6)   11% of 7
7)   53% of 12366
8)   3.2% of 2.6

Compute the discount and the new sale price for each.
1) A shirt priced at $23 with a 20% discount
2) A blouse priced at $26.95 with a 10% discount

Compute the sales tax and the price plus sales tax
3) Radio $19.75 with a 5% sales tax
4) Computer $239.16 with a 6% sales tax

Find the percent.
5) Karen spent $29.75 of her savings for a coat. Find the percent spent if her savings was $85.
6) Patrice earned $36 one week tutoring. She spent $3.96 for school supplies. What percent did Patrice spend on school supplies?

Find the earnings.
7) Kirk saves 15% of his part-time earnings for clothes. If he saves $8.25 for clothes, how much does he earn?
8) Luke saves 30% of his weekly earnings for college. If he saves $13.50 weekly, how much does he earn per week?

Construct a circle graph for each budget.

9) Housing 25%
Transportation 10%
Other 65%

10) Housing 30%
Food 20%
Entertainment 20%
Other 30%

CHAPTER 14

WORKING WITH INTEREST

Banks and finance companies charge *interest* for the money that you borrow from them. The loan may be in the form of a bank loan like a home mortgage or in the form of credit card charges. Interest is charged for both kinds of loans.

Banks pay you interest for the use of the money you have put into your savings account. This interest is calculated the same way that the interest on your loans is calculated. The only difference is that you receive the interest.

The mathematical skill needed to work with interest is the ability to multiply money — the principal — by a percent — the rate — times the time. You may need to round your answer to two places because interest is money.

SIMPLE INTEREST

Interest is calculated by multiplying the *principal* times the *rate* of interest times the *time*. The principal is the amount of the loan or the amount in your savings account. The rate is a percent paid for each time period. The time is the length of time that you had the loan or the time the money was in the account.

John's sports car will cost $2478.93. His uncle agreed to loan John the money at a simple interest rate of $18\frac{1}{2}$ % per year for $2\frac{1}{4}$ years. How much simple interest will John have to pay?

Example:

Compute the simple interest on $2478.93 at $18\frac{1}{2}$ % per year for $2\frac{1}{4}$ years.

$$\text{Interest} = \text{Principal} \times \text{Rate} \times \text{Time in Years}$$
$$\text{Interest} = \$2478.93 \times .185 \times 2.25$$

Step 1:

$2478.93	Principal
× .185	Interest Rate
$458.60205	
$458.60	Rounded interest for 1 year

Step 2:

$458.60	Interest
× 2.25	Time in years
$1031.85	Total interest

Remember, the months must be converted to a decimal.

Example:

3 years, 7 months = 3.58, using the chart at right.

Converting Months to Years		
Months	Fractional Part of Year	Rounded Decimals
1	1/12	.08
2	2/12	.17
3	3/12	.25
4	4/12	.33
5	5/12	.42
6	6/12	.5
7	7/12	.58
8	8/12	.67
9	9/12	.75
10	10/12	.83
11	11/12	.92

EXERCISE A.   Find the products.

1) $60 × 4% × 2 years

2) $120 × 6% × 1 year

3) $250 × 6% × 4 years

4) $96 × 3% × 5 years

5) $320 × 7% × 4 years

6) $136 × 3% × 3 years

EXERCISE B.   Find the simple interest. Annual interest rates are given.

1) Compute the interest for a principal of $165 with a rate of interest of 6% for 4 years.

2) Compute the interest for a principal of $235 with a rate of interest of 7% for 3 years.

3) Compute the interest for 5 years on a principal of $86.45 at 7% interest.

4) $80 at 6% for 3 years

5) $36 at 7% for 3 years

6) $125 at 5% for 2 years

7) $17 at 8% for 3 years

8) $38 at 6% for 6 months

9) $23.40 at 5% for 6 months

10) $102.26 at 7% for 2 years

11) $16.95 at 5% for 4 years

12) $2065 at 6% for 2 years

13) $191 at 8% for $3 \frac{1}{2}$ years

14) $103 at 10% for 8 years

15) $39.95 at 10% for 2 years

16) $285 at 10% for 10 years

17) $104 at 5% for 8 months

18) $49.92 at 5% for 4 months

19) $1000 at 7% for 10 years

20) $263 at 9% for $2 \frac{1}{2}$ years

21) $8 at 8% for $3 \frac{1}{4}$ years

22) $82.43 at 6% for 4 years

23) $52.63 at 8% for 2 years

24) $1095 at 9% for 6 months

25) $92 at 9% for 8 months

The rate of interest may contain a fraction. To compute the interest, change the fraction to its decimal equivalent. Then, multiply.

Example:
Compute the simple interest on a principal of $200 at $6\frac{1}{2}$ % per year for 2 years.

$$\text{Interest} = \text{Principal} \times \text{Rate} \times \text{Time}$$

$$6\frac{1}{2}\ \% = .065$$

$200	Principal
× .065	Rate of interest
1.000	
12.000	
$13.000	Interest for 1 year
$13.00	Interest for 1 year
× 2	
$26.00	Interest for 2 years

$$\frac{1}{4} = .25$$

$$\frac{1}{2} = .5$$

$$\frac{3}{4} = .75$$

EXERCISE C.   Find the simple interest. Annual interest rates are given.

1) $400 at $8\frac{1}{2}$ % for 2 years

2) $175 at $6\frac{1}{4}$ % for 2 years

3) $200 at $6\frac{3}{4}$ % for 3 years

4) $75 at $6\frac{1}{2}$ % for 6 months

5) $62 at $7\frac{3}{4}$ % for 9 years

6) $380 at $6\frac{3}{4}$ % for 5 years

7) $1800 at $9\frac{3}{4}$ % for 1 year

8) $350 at $7\frac{1}{4}$ % for 3 years

9) $395 at $7\frac{3}{4}$ % for 2 years

10) $80 at $8\frac{1}{2}$ % for 6 months

11) $267 at $9\frac{3}{4}$ % for 3 years

12) $132 at $5\frac{1}{4}$ % for 5 years

13) $17 at $9\frac{1}{4}$ % for 2 years

14) $500 at $6\frac{1}{4}$ % for 4 years

COMPOUND INTEREST

You can earn compound interest when the bank pays interest on the principal and on the interest already earned on money in a savings account.

Example:

John deposited $150 in his new account and received 6% interest compounded quarterly. What was his balance at the end of one year?

$$\text{Interest} = \text{Principal} \times \text{Rate} \times \text{Time}$$

First Quarter:

a)
	$150	Principal
×	.015	(6% divided by 4)
	$2.250	Interest

b)
	$150.00	Principal
+	2.25	Interest
	$152.25	New principal

Second Quarter:

c)
	$152.25	Principal
×	.015	Rate
	$2.28375	Interest

d)
	$152.25	Principal
+	2.28	Interest
	$154.53	New principal

Third Quarter:

e)
	$154.53	Principal
×	.015	Rate
	$2.31795	Interest

f)
	$154.53	Principal
+	2.32	Interest
	$156.85	New principal

Fourth Quarter:

g)
	$156.85	Principal
×	.015	Rate
	$2.35275	Interest

h)
	$156.85	Principal
+	2.35	Interest
	$159.20	New principal

The balance at the end of one year was $159.20.

EXERCISE A.   Find the interest compounded quarterly and the new balance at the end of one year.

1) $200 at 8%   7) $850 at 12%

2) $500 at 6%   8) $960 at 12%

3) $250 at 10%   9) $2000 at 7%

4) $300 at 10%   10) $1500 at 9%

5) $450 at 8%   11) $1600 at 8%

6) $1000 at 9%   12) $145 at 10%

BORROWING MONEY

The Subtraction Method. Some lenders of money subtract the interest due from the total amount that they lend. The borrower does not receive the full amount, but he pays back the full amount.

Example:

Greg wants to borrow $1000 at 12%, making 12 monthly payments. How much is each payment?

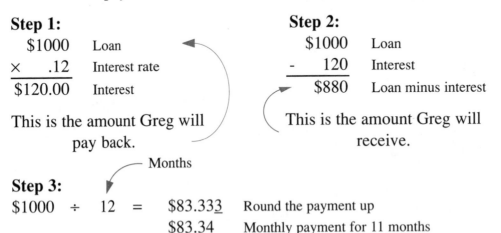

Step 1:
$$\begin{array}{ll} \$1000 & \text{Loan} \\ \times\quad .12 & \text{Interest rate} \\ \hline \$120.00 & \text{Interest} \end{array}$$

This is the amount Greg will pay back.

Step 2:
$$\begin{array}{ll} \$1000 & \text{Loan} \\ -\quad 120 & \text{Interest} \\ \hline \$880 & \text{Loan minus interest} \end{array}$$

This is the amount Greg will receive.

Step 3:

$1000 ÷ 12 = $83.33<u>3</u>   Round the payment up

                   $83.34   Monthly payment for 11 months

Step 4:

Notice that $83.34 × 12 = $1000.08.

The last payment, then, is $83.34 - .08, or $83.26.

EXERCISE A. Find the monthly payment. Write the amount of the last payment if it differs from the first payment.

1) $600 at 10% for 12 months

2) $700 at 12% for 12 months

3) $950 at 12% for 18 months

4) $550 at 10% for 12 months

5) $12,000 at 14% for 6 months

6) $1000 at 10% for 18 months

7) $1500 at 10% for 12 months

8) $1100 at 12% for 18 months

9) $1200 at 12% for 12 months

10) $1600 at 14% for 10 months

11) $450 at 16% for 12 months

12) $900 at 10% for 12 months

The Addition Method. Some lenders add the interest to the amount of the loan. The borrower pays back the full amount of the loan plus interest.

Example:

Lisa wants to borrow $1000 at 12%, making 12 monthly payments. How much is each payment?

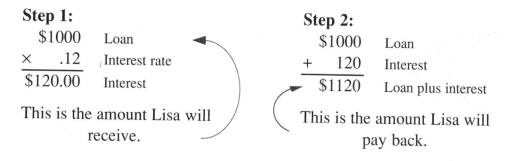

Step 1:

$1000	Loan
× .12	Interest rate
$120.00	Interest

This is the amount Lisa will receive.

Step 2:

$1000	Loan
+ 120	Interest
$1120	Loan plus interest

This is the amount Lisa will pay back.

Step 3:

$1120 ÷ 12 = $93.33<u>3</u> Round the payment up

$93.34 Monthly payment for 11 months

Step 4:

Notice that $93.34 × 12 = $1120.08.

The last payment, then, is $93.34 - .08, or $93.26.

EXERCISE B.   Find the monthly payment. Write the amount of the last payment if it differs from the first payment. Use the addition method.

1) $600 at 10% for 12 months
2) $800 at 12% for 18 months
3) $1200 at 8% for 6 months
4) $950 at 9% for 10 months
5) $75 at 10% for 12 months
6) $200 at 20% for 12 months
7) $500 at 12% for 6 months
8) $150 at 8% for 10 months
9) $1000 at 7% for 8 months
10) $1500 at 14% for 10 months
11) $2500 at 15% for 12 months
12) $230 at 8% for 24 months
13) $2500 at 10% for 10 months

EXERCISE C.   Find the monthly payment. Write the amount of the last payment if it differs from the first payment. Use the subtraction method.

1) $500 at 12% for 12 months
2) $750 at 10% for 12 months
3) $650 at 12% for 12 months
4) $850 at 9% for 12 months
5) $780 at 10% for 18 months
6) $900 at 10% for 12 months
7) $900 at 9% for 18 months
8) $800 at 14% for 18 months
9) $500 at 8% for 12 months
10) $1200 at 6% for 10 months
11) $1000 at 10% for 18 months
12) $1100 at 10% for 12 months
13) $1300 at 9% for 10 months
14) $1250 at 15% for 10 months

EXERCISE D.   Find the monthly payment. Write the amount of the last payment if it differs from the first payment. Use the addition method.

1) $2000 at 8% for 18 months
2) $1900 at 10% for 18 months
3) $1850 at 14% for 12 months
4) $2000 at 12% for 6 months
5) $1700 at 16% for 10 months
6) $1700 at 10% for 12 months
7) $1600 at 12% for 12 months
8) $400 at 12% for 12 months
9) $350 at 9% for 12 months
10) $450 at 14% for 18 months
11) $960 at 10% for 12 months
12) $825 at 10% for 6 months
13) $1350 at 14% for 6 months
14) $1735 at 16% for 10 months

CREDIT

Buying with *credit* is like borrowing money. You buy now and pay later. When you pay later, you pay a percent of interest for the use of the money. This interest is charged to your account each month. The first month is usually interest-free.

For example, Mariah purchased a lawn mower on sale for $205 on the condition that she make monthly payments of $30 per month with a finance charge of $1\frac{1}{2}$ % on the unpaid balance. She will make her first payment on the first day of January.

Step 1:

$205	Balance
- 30	January payment
$175	Balance for February

Step 2:

$175	Previous balance
× .015	Finance rate
$2.625	Finance charge
$2.63	Rounded to $2.63

Step 3:

$175.00	Previous balance
+ 2.63	Finance charge
$177.63	Before payment

Step 4:

$177.63	Before payment
- 30.00	Payment
$147.63	New balance for the following month

EXERCISE A.   Complete the information for this chart for the lawn mower.

Month	Previous Balance	Finance Charge	Before Payment	Monthly Payment	New Balance
Jan.	$205.00	$ —	$205.00	$30	$175.00
Feb.	$175.00	$2.63	$177.63	$30	$147.63
March	$147.63	$2.21	$149.84	$30	$119.84
April	$119.84				
May					
June					
July					

EXERCISE B.   Complete the information for these charts.

1) Rick purchased his school clothes for a total of $111. He agreed to make $15 monthly payments with the first month interest-free. His finance charge will be $1\frac{1}{2}$ % on the unpaid balance.

Month	Previous Balance	Finance Charge	Before Payment	Monthly Payment	New Balance
Aug.	$111.00	$ —	$111.00	$15	$96.00
Sept.	$96.00	$1.44	$97.44	$15	$82.44
Oct.					
Nov.					
Dec.					
Jan.					
Feb.					
March					
April					

2) Nicole purchased a birthday gift for her mother costing $143. She agreed to make payments of $20 per month with a finance charge of 2% on the unpaid balance. Her first month will be interest-free.

Month	Previous Balance	Finance Charge	Before Payment	Monthly Payment	New Balance
Feb.	$143.00	$ —	$143.00	$20	$123.00
March	$123.00	$2.46	$125.46	$20	$105.46
April	$105.46				
May					
June					
July					
Aug.					
Sept.					
Oct.					

Calculator Practice 14

Budgeting often requires you to find a percentage of earnings. Calculate the percentages for the budgets below. Round your answers to the nearest cent.

Megan's Budget With $200 per Week		Amount
Entertainment	5%	
Food	20%	
Car	25%	
Rent	19%	
Savings	15%	
Miscellaneous	16%	

Rick's Budget With $175 per Week		Amount
Rent	25%	
Car	20%	
Savings	10%	
Food	15%	
Clothes	5%	
Miscellaneous	25%	

Computer Practice 14

   This program will help you find percentages that are rounded to the nearest hundredth. (See Appendix for more information.)

```
10     PRINT    "FINDING THE PERCENTAGE ROUNDED TO THE NEAR-
               EST HUNDREDTH"
20     PRINT "TYPE THE RATE WITHOUT THE PERCENT SIGN."
30     INPUT A
40     PRINT "TYPE THE BASE."
50     INPUT B
60     X = INT(A * B + .5)/100
70     PRINT "PERCENTAGE = ";X
80     END
```

COMPUTER EXERCISE.   Use a computer to find the percentages.

1)   1.5% of 26.358

2)   2.6% of $55.88

3)   53.6% of 1.703

4)   .6% of 2.9

5)   7.3% of .89

6)   90.2% of 18.763

CHAPTER TEST

Compute the simple interest.

1) $125 at 10% for 3 years

2) $110 at 7% for 6 months

3) $290 at $6\frac{1}{2}$ % for 5 years

4) $206 at $7\frac{1}{4}$ % for 2 years

Compute the compound interest quarterly.

5) $300 at 8% for 1 year

6) $275 at 10% for 1 year

Complete the information in the chart on credit buying.

7) A purchase of $175 with monthly payments of $50 and a finance charge of $1\frac{1}{2}$ % on the unpaid balance. The first month will be interest-free.

Month	Previous Balance	Finance Charge	Before Payment	Monthly Payment	New Balance
Jan.	$175.00	$ —	$175.00	$50.00	$125.00
Feb.	$125.00	$1.88		$50.00	
March				$50.00	
April					$000.00

Find the payments.

8) Use the addition method to compute the first and last payments on a loan of $175 at 10% for 12 months.

9) Use the subtraction method to compute the first and last payments on a loan of $200 at 15% for 10 months.

10) Use the addition method to compute the first and last payments on a loan of $100 at 8% for 6 months.

CHAPTER 15

INSURANCE

People buy *insurance* so that they will be protected from financial loss in the event of an accident or illness. There are many types of insurance, including health, home, life, and auto.

In order to understand how the insurance companies determine the amount that you must pay for the insurance, you will need to be able to read charts. Many of the charts will give the cost of insurance per $100 of *coverage*. Because of this, you will also need to be able to tell how many 100s are in a given amount.

Example:

How many $100s are in $35,000? $2,600? $23,420?

$$\begin{array}{r} 350 \\ 100\overline{)35000} \end{array} \qquad \begin{array}{r} 26 \\ 100\overline{)2600} \end{array} \qquad \begin{array}{r} 234.2 \\ 100\overline{)23420.0} \end{array}$$

EXERCISE A.   Tell how many $100s are in each amount below.

1) $48,000

2) $52,000

3) $60,000

4) $7,300

5) $74,000

6) $50,300

7) $47,000

8) $320,000

9) $3,840

10) $30,400

11) $560

12) $50,430

13) $48,070

14) $30,610

15) $4,372

16) $5,930

17) $39,400

18) $7,380

19) $9,180

20) $381,270

21) $4,350

Health Care Insurance

PLAN A: Up to $33.33 a day ($1000 for every 30 days) from the first day of covered accidents or illnesses.

Age at Enrollment	Monthly Premium per Adult
16-39	$7.90
40-44	$8.90
45-49	$9.90
50-54	$10.90
55-64	$11.40
65-74	$11.90
75-79	$13.40
80 & over	$15.90

Add $5.70 per month to cover all unmarried children from birth through 18 years old. If husband and wife are covered, add $2.50 per month for maternity benefits.

PLAN B: Up to $33.33 a day ($1000 for every 30 days) from the first day of covered accidents or the fifth day of illnesses.

• This plan pays the same benefits as Plan A but at lower premiums.

Age at Enrollment	Monthly Premium per Adult
16-39	$4.40
40-44	$5.40
45-49	$6.40
50-54	$7.40
55-64	$8.90
65-74	$9.40
75-79	$10.40
80 & over	$12.90

Add $3.65 per month to cover all unmarried children from birth through 18 years old. If husband and wife are covered, add $2.50 per month for maternity benefits.

PLAN C: Up to $20.00 a day ($600 for every 30 days) from the first day of covered accidents or illnesses.

• This plan pays 60% of the Plan A benefits.

Age at Enrollment	Monthly Premium per Adult
16-39	$5.10
40-44	$5.70
45-49	$6.30
50-54	$6.90
55-64	$7.20
65-74	$7.50
75-79	$8.40
80 & over	$9.90

Add $3.42 per month to cover all unmarried children from birth through 18 years old. If husband and wife are covered, add $2.50 per month for maternity benefits.

HEALTH INSURANCE

Families buy health insurance so that they will not need to worry about how they will pay their doctors' and hospital bills if they should have an accident or become ill. Most health care companies offer a variety of health insurance plans. More extensive coverage costs more money. The amount of money that you pay for the health insurance is called the *premium*. You can determine the premium by reading the insurance premium chart.

For example, George Woods is 42 years old. His wife, Susan, is 39 years old. They and their two children are enrolled in Plan B of the Health Care Program. They do not have maternity benefits. How much is their monthly premium? Use the chart on page 225.

$5.40
$4.40
+ $3.65
―――――
$13.45   Monthly premium

EXERCISE A.   Find the monthly premium for each coverage described below. Do not include maternity benefits unless they are mentioned.

1)   Single woman 43 years old, Plan A

2)   Single man 51 years old, Plan C

3)   Husband 28 years old, wife 27 years old, Plan B

4)   Husband 41 years old, wife 38 years old, three children, maternity benefits, Plan B

5)   Husband 54 years old, wife 52 years old, Plan A

6)   Husband 32 years old, wife 29 years old, maternity benefits, Plan C

7)   Single man 56 years old, Plan B

8)   Husband 63 years old, wife 65 years old, Plan A

9)   Husband 27 years old, wife 27 years old, maternity benefits, Plan B

10)   Husband 36 years old, wife 33, two children, Plan A

Major Medical Insurance. Many health care plans place limits on covered expenses. The plan may not cover hospital stays over 120 days or doctors' bills over $350 per year. Because of these limits, many companies provide their employees with *major medical insurance* coverage. A family that has a health care policy and a major medical policy will be well protected for most illnesses or accidents. Payroll deductions can be made weekly, semimonthly, or monthly from your paycheck.

Rest Easy Major Medical Program
Semimonthly Payroll Deductions

Employee only	$2.22
Employee and wife only..	$4.98
Employee and child or children only	$3.67
Employee and wife and child or children...........................	$6.43
Employee and husband only	$4.27
Employee and husband and child or children	$5.72

Example:

Morgan Collins and her husband are enrolled in the Rest Easy Major Medical Program. What is their annual premium?

$$\begin{array}{r} \$4.27 \\ \times \quad 24 \\ \hline 17\ 08 \\ 85\ 4 \quad \\ \hline \$102.48 \end{array}$$ Annual premium

EXERCISE B. Find the annual premium for each family described below. The person named is the employee.

1) Joe Kassa and his wife and one child
2) Bertha Guthrie and her husband and one child
3) Joanne Verando and one child
4) Gus Harrington
5) David Henski and his wife

---

6) Louis Kohn and his three children

7) Mary Radcliffe and her husband and two children

8) Henry Jones and his wife and their six children

9) Jim Gleason

10) Karen Jackson and her husband

HOME INSURANCE

Most families insure their homes against possible loss by buying insurance. If the house should catch fire, the insurance company would pay for the damages up to the amount of the insurance coverage. You should insure your house for the full value of the house plus its contents. The first step in determining how much the house is worth is to do a *unit count* for your house.

Count 1 for Each Unit Below:	Count 1/2 for Each Unit Below:
Kitchen	Half Bathroom
Dining Room	(1 or 2 fixtures)
Living Room	One-car Garage
Bedroom	Dinette
Bathroom	Breakfast Nook
(3 or more fixtures)	Unfinished Basement
Den or Study	Unfinished Attic
Family Room	Enclosed Porch
Utility Room	Fireplace
Finished Attic	
Finished Basement	
Two-Car Garage	
Central Air Conditioning	

Example:

What is the unit count of this house?

1 Kitchen
1 Dining Room
1 Living Room
3 Bedrooms
1 Bathroom
1 Family Room
1 Utility Room
1 Two-Car Garage
$\frac{1}{2}$ Half Bathroom
$\frac{1}{2}$ Fireplace

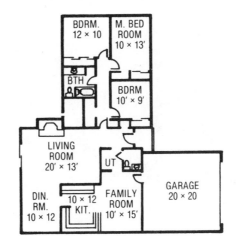

---

11 Unit Count

EXERCISE A.   Determine the unit count for each house below.

1)

2)

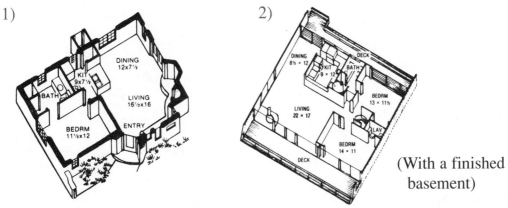

(With a finished basement)

3)   A two-story house with 3 bedrooms, 2 full bathrooms, living room, dining room, kitchen, den, unfinished basement, central air conditioning, finished attic, and one-car garage.

Construction Class. After you have determined the size of the house by doing a unit count, you must decide what type of house you have. Insurance companies have divided houses into four *construction classes*. When you know the unit count and the construction class, you find the house's *base cost* from a chart.

Class I
Plain design
Stock-type house
Tract-type house
Low cost
Just meets building codes
Dining area part of living room or kitchen
No special purpose rooms

Class II
Simple design
Standard plans
Some ornamentation
Average quality
Meets or exceeds building codes
Dining room
Den or family room
Most older homes are in this class.

Class III
Individual design
Modified plans
Built for a specific buyer
Average to above average work
Meets or exceeds building codes
Den or family room
Foyer common

Class IV

One-of-a-kind design   Unique floor plan
Architect's plans   Large rooms and foyer
Above average work   Many special rooms
Exceeds building codes

Unit Count	CONSTRUCTION CLASS			
	I	II	III	IV
6	$20,900	$26,300	$33,400	$40,100
6 1/2	$22,900	$29,000	$36,000	$44,000
7	$24,100	$30,600	$39,300	$45,700
7 1/2	$26,200	$33,200	$42,500	$46,900
8	$27,800	$35,100	$44,900	$50,700
8 1/2	$29,900	$37,700	$48,100	$57,400
9	$31,400	$39,700	$50,500	$60,300
9 1/2	$33,400	$42,300	$53,700	$64,200
10	$35,500	$45,000	$56,200	$67,000
10 1/2	$37,700	$47,600	$59,500	$70,800
11	$40,100	$49,500	$61,800	$73,700
11 1/2	$40,800	$51,600	$64,500	$76,900
12	—	$54,500	$67,400	$80,400
12 1/2	—	$57,100	$70,700	$84,300
13	—	$59,600	$73,000	$93,700
13 1/2	—	$62,300	$76,400	$97,700
14	—	$65,000	$78,800	$98,600
14 1/2	—	$67,600	$82,100	$99,700

EXERCISE B.   Use the chart to find the base cost of each house.

	Unit Count	Construction Class	Base Cost
1)	10 ½	III	____
2)	12	II	____
3)	7	I	____
4)	13	IV	____
5)	14 ½	IV	____
6)	6 ½	II	____
7)	11	III	____
8)	8	II	____

Replacement Cost. Once you know the base cost of your home, you can find the house's *replacement cost* by using a location multiplier. A location multiplier is used because the same house can be built for different prices in different areas. The cost of labor and materials varies from location to location. Insurance companies have researched these variations in building costs and organized their findings by ZIP codes.

Example:

A house of construction class III has a unit count of $10\frac{1}{2}$. The ZIP code is 40412. What is its replacement cost?

From the chart:
Unit count is $10\frac{1}{2}$
Class III
Base cost = $59,500
ZIP code is <u>404</u>12
Location multiplier = 1.02

Location By First 3 Digits of ZIP Code	Location Multiplier
Kentucky	
400-402	1.02
403-405	1.02
406-410	1.01
411-422	.99
423-424	1.01
425-427	.97
Ohio	
430-433	1.06
434, 436	1.16
435	1.12
437-439	1.04
440-443	1.10
444-450	1.08
451-455, 458	1.07
456-457	1.14
Indiana	
460-462	1.06
463-464	1.09
465-466	1.04
467-468	1.01
469, 478-479	.96
470-475	1.05
476-477	1.03

$59,500
×   1.02
─────────
119000
595000
─────────
$60690.00

The replacement cost is $60,690.

EXERCISE C.   Use the ZIP code chart and the construction class chart to find the replacement cost of each house.

	Unit Count	Class	ZIP Code	Replacement Cost
1)	12	II	42416	___
2)	$13\frac{1}{2}$	III	46307	___
3)	10	I	44321	___
4)	$7\frac{1}{2}$	I	43516	___
5)	$12\frac{1}{2}$	IV	45624	___
6)	12	II	46602	___
7)	$12\frac{1}{2}$	III	47933	___
8)	9	II	42620	___
9)	$13\frac{1}{2}$	IV	43414	___
10)	6	I	41607	___
11)	$8\frac{1}{2}$	IV	46401	___
12)	$11\frac{1}{2}$	III	47221	___

Calculator Practice 15

Insurance premiums are often given as a yearly rate. It might be necessary to budget your earnings to make your yearly payment.

CALCULATOR EXERCISE. Use the calculator to divide the yearly payments listed by 52 paydays. Round the payments to the nearest cent.

1)	$385	7)	$201.34
2)	$272	8)	$89.90
3)	$776.80	9)	$149.50
4)	$105	10)	$200
5)	$125	11)	$136.75
6)	$603	12)	$492.50

FIRE INSURANCE

After you have found the replacement cost of your home, you can determine how much insurance to buy. Many people insure their homes for replacement cost plus the value of the items in the home. Insurance is also available for people who live in apartments. The yearly charge for the insurance is called the premium. The amount of insurance protection is called the *face value* of the policy. The premium is found by multiplying the rate per $100 times the number of hundreds in the face value of the policy. The rate per $100 varies according to the type of policy.

Example:

Face value: $23,500
Rate per $100: $.68
There are 235 hundreds in $23,500.

$$
\begin{array}{r}
235 \\
\times \quad \$.68 \\
\hline
\$159.80
\end{array}
$$

The yearly premium is $159.80.

EXERCISE A. Find the yearly premium for each fire insurance policy.

	Face Value	Rate per $100	Yearly Premium
1)	$52,300	$.96	____
2)	$20,700	$.73	____
3)	$38,000	$.84	____
4)	$71,450	$.88	____
5)	$46,700	$.92	____
6)	$56,700	$.80	____
7)	$48,800	$.92	____
8)	$67,500	$.93	____
9)	$46,730	$.87	____
10)	$79,400	$.96	____
11)	$71,120	$.78	____
12)	$86,200	$.99	____

AUTO INSURANCE

Auto liability insurance protects the owner of a car against claims arising from his or her car being involved in an accident. *Liability* insurance can cover both bodily injury and property damage. The premium that you pay for this protection, or coverage, is determined by the amount of protection and the region in which you live.

Coverage for a 50/100/25 Policy

Maximum of $50,000 for claim of 1 injured person →

50/100/25

← Maximum of $25,000 for property damage

↑
Maximum of $100,000 for claim of 2 or more injured people

	Liability Insurance Rates						
	Bodily Injury				Property Damage		
Region	10/20	20/40	25/50	50/100	5,000	10,000	25,000
1	$101	$139	$152	$182	$68	$71	$73
2	$59	$81	$89	$106	$52	$55	$56
3	$50	$69	$75	$90	$56	$59	$60
4	$40	$55	$60	$72	$48	$50	$52
5	$53	$73	$80	$95	$47	$49	$51

Example:

Jake lives in Region 3. His coverage is 50/100/25. Using the chart, Jake's premium is $90 plus $60, or $150.

EXERCISE A.   Determine the amount of the basic premium for each liability insurance policy.

	Coverage	**Region**	**Premium**
1)	20/40/5	4	___
2)	20/40/25	1	___
3)	20/40/10	3	___
4)	25/50/10	2	___
5)	10/20/10	5	___
6)	20/40/25	3	___
7)	50/100/25	3	___
8)	20/40/5	2	___
9)	50/100/10	1	___
10)	10/20/10	3	___
11)	10/20/25	4	___
12)	25/50/25	2	___

Once the auto insurance agent has determined the basic premium for auto liability insurance coverage, he consults a rate factor table. Women pay less than men do for the same insurance coverage. You will pay less for insurance if you drive the car for pleasure or farm use than if you drive the car to work each day. You will pay more if you use your car for business.

Age of Driver	Sex	Pleasure Use	Drives Less Than 10 mi. to Work	Drives 10 mi. or More to Work	Car Used for Work	Farm Use
17	M	1.80	1.90	2.20	2.30	1.55
	F	1.55	1.65	1.95	2.05	1.30
18	M	1.70	1.80	2.10	2.20	1.45
	F	1.40	1.50	1.80	1.90	1.15
19	M	1.60	1.70	2.00	2.10	1.35
	F	1.25	1.35	1.65	1.75	1.00
20	M	1.50	1.60	1.90	2.00	1.25
	F	1.10	1.20	1.50	1.60	.85

Example:

Sara and Eric both have a basic insurance premium of $131. Each is 19 years old and drives 7 miles to work. Sara's premium is $176.85 (131 × 1.35). Eric's premium is 222.70 (131 × 1.70).

EXERCISE B. Find each person's insurance premium by multiplying the basic premium by the appropriate factor from the table.

1) Heidi is 17 years old. She drives 6 miles to work. Her basic premium is $135.

2) Michael's basic premium is $128. He uses the car only on the farm. He is 17 years old.

3) Gene is 18 years old. His basic premium is $208. He uses the car only for pleasure.

4) Judy is 20 years old. Her basic premium is $147. She drives 16 miles to work.

5) Rudy drives 8 miles to work. He is 19 years old. His basic premium is $183.

6) Richard is 20 years old. He uses the car in his work. His basic premium is $236.

7) Angela is 18 years old. She drives 10 miles to work. Her basic premium is $188.

8) Ronny drives 9 miles to work. He is 20 years old. His basic premium is $306.

9) Ed is 17 years old. He uses his car for pleasure. His basic premium is $294.

10) Sheila is 19 years old. She drives 14 miles to work. Her basic premium is $289.

LIFE INSURANCE

Families buy life insurance to protect the dependents of the insured person. If the insured person dies, his *beneficiary* is paid the face value of the life insurance policy.

There are different kinds of life insurance that a person can buy. The four basic kinds of life insurance are:

1. **Term Insurance**. Premiums are paid only for a certain time. The *policyholder* is insured only during the stated time. Benefits are paid only if the policyholder dies during the term of insurance.

2. **Ordinary Life**. Premiums are paid until the policyholder dies. When the policyholder dies, the beneficiary is paid the face value of the policy.

3. **Limited-Payment Life Insurance**. The policyholder is insured until he dies. Premiums are paid for a limited period of time (20 or 30 years, usually). This kind of insurance is also called 20-payment or 30-payment life insurance.

4. **Endowment**. The policyholder pays premiums for a limited period of time (20 or 30 years, usually). At the end of this period of time, the policyholder is paid the face value of the policy. If the policyholder dies during the payment period, the beneficiary is paid the face value of the policy.

The premiums are the lowest for term insurance. Ordinary life insurance costs more. Limited-payment insurance is more expensive. The most expensive insurance is endowment insurance.

Here are some premium tables for the four types of life insurance described:

| Age | | Annual Premium Per $1000 of Term Insurance | | | |
| Age | | 5-Year Term Policy | | 10-Year Term Policy | |
Male	Female	$5000-$9999	$10,000-$19,999	$5000-$9999	$10,000-$19,999
20	23	$6.44	$5.69	$6.51	$5.76
25	28	$6.59	$5.84	$6.72	$5.97
30	33	$6.88	$6.13	$7.19	$6.44
35	38	$7.56	$6.81	$8.27	$7.52
40	43	$9.11	$8.36	$10.24	$9.49
45	48	$11.60	$10.85	$13.43	$12.68
50	53	$15.66	$14.91	$18.47	$17.72
55	58	$21.95	$21.20	$26.28	$25.53
60	63	$31.80	$31.05	$38.40	$37.65

| Age | | Annual Life Insurance Premium Rates per $1000 | | | | | |
| Age | | Ordinary Life | | 20-Payment Life | | 20-Year Endowment | |
Male	Female	$5000-$9999	$10,000-$19,999	$5000-$9999	$10,000-$19,999	$5000-$9999	$10,000-$19,999
20	23	$15.07	$14.32	$22.90	$22.15	$46.70	$45.95
25	28	$17.08	$16.33	$25.43	$24.68	$46.93	$46.18
30	33	$19.63	$18.88	$28.42	$27.67	$47.36	$46.61
35	38	$22.94	$22.19	$32.02	$31.27	$48.19	$47.44
40	43	$27.25	$26.50	$36.40	$35.65	$49.66	$48.91
45	48	$32.85	$32.10	$41.72	$40.97	$52.01	$51.26
50	53	$40.23	$39.48	$48.33	$47.58	$55.76	$55.01
55	58	$49.93	$49.18	$56.64	$55.89	$61.64	$60.89
60	63	$62.47	$61.72	$67.70	$66.85	$70.59	$69.84

You can see from the premium tables that women pay less for insurance than men do. Also, the older you are when you buy insurance, the more you pay.

In order to determine the annual premium, you find the type of insurance in the charts, find the correct age and sex, and read the rate per $1000 of face value. You multiply this rate by the number of 1000s in the face value of the policy.

Example:

What is the annual premium for a 38-year-old woman if she buys $15,000 of 20-payment life insurance?

From the chart: Rate per $1000 = $31.27

Number of 1000s in $15,000 = 15

$$\begin{array}{r} \$31.27 \\ \times \quad 15 \\ \hline \$469.05 \end{array}$$ Annual premium

EXERCISE A. Find the annual premium for each life insurance policy below.

1) 45-year-old man, $10,000 5-year term policy
2) 48-year-old woman, $14,000 20-year life policy
3) 40-year-old man, $6,000 ordinary life policy
4) 58-year-old woman, $14,000 10-year term policy
5) 33-year-old woman, $15,000 20-year endowment policy
6) 20-year-old man, $17,000 20-year endowment policy
7) 40-year-old man, $19,000 20-payment life policy
8) 50-year-old man, $16,000 10-year term policy
9) 50-year-old man, $13,000 ordinary life policy
10) 28-year-old woman, $17,000 20-year endowment policy
11) 38-year-old woman, $9,000 ordinary life policy
12) 30-year-old man, $8,900 10-year term policy

Computer Practice 15

Many people pay their insurance premiums once a year. They may put aside a portion of their earnings every payday to be saved for the insurance premium. This program will help determine the amount to be budgeted. (See Appendix for more information.)

```
10   PRINT "DIVIDING YEARLY PREMIUM BY NUMBER OF PAYDAYS"
20   PRINT "YEARLY PAYMENT IS "
30   INPUT "$";A
40   PRINT "NUMBER OF PAYDAYS IS "
50   INPUT P
60   IF A * P = 0 THEN 80
70   PRINT "$"; INT(A/P * 100 + .5)/100
80   END
```

COMPUTER EXERCISE.   Use a computer to find the amount to be budgeted.

	Premium	Paydays
1)	$295	52
2)	$175	48
3)	$602	26
4)	$382.75	26
5)	$780	40
6)	$542.50	52
7)	$172	52
8)	$103	50

CHAPTER TEST

How many $100s are contained in each amount below?

1) $57,000

2) $465,400

3) $56,480

Use this chart of payroll deductions for major medical insurance to find the annual premium for each family described below. The person named is the employee.

Rest Easy Major Medical Program — Semimonthly Payroll Deductions	
Employee only	$2.22
Employee and wife only	$4.98
Employee and child or children only	$3.67
Employee and wife and child or children	$6.43
Employee and husband only	$4.27
Employee and husband and child or children	$5.72

4) Frank Nemik and his wife and two children

5) Linda Carter and her husband

6) Max Bauer and his son

Answer these questions about the replacement cost.

7) The base cost of a house is $48,600 and the location multiplier is 1.08. What is the house's replacement cost?

8) The base cost of a house is $67,400 and the location multiplier is .97. What is the house's replacement cost?

Find the yearly premium for each fire insurance policy.

9) The policy's face value is $52,400. The rate per $100 is $.96.

10) The policy's face value is $67,000. The rate per $100 is $.80.

Use this rate chart to find the basic premium for each auto liability insurance policy described.

	Liability Insurance Rates						
	Bodily Injury				Property Damage		
Region	10/20	20/40	25/50	50/100	5,000	10,000	25,000
1	$101	$139	$152	$182	$68	$71	$73
2	$59	$81	$89	$106	$52	$55	$56
3	$50	$69	$75	$90	$56	$59	$60
4	$40	$55	$60	$72	$48	$50	$52

11) 20/40/10 coverage; Region 3
12) 25/50/25 coverage; Region 2
13) 10/20/5 coverage; Region 4

Find each person's insurance premium by multiplying the basic premium by the appropriate factor from this table.

Age of Driver	Sex	Pleasure Use	Drives Less Than 10 mi. to Work	Drives 10 mi. or More to Work	Car Used for Work
17	M	1.80	1.90	2.20	2.30
	F	1.55	1.65	1.95	2.05
18	M	1.70	1.80	2.10	2.20
	F	1.40	1.50	1.80	1.90
19	M	1.60	1.70	2.00	2.10
	F	1.25	1.35	1.65	1.75

14) Mary is 18 years old. She drives 12 miles to work. Her basic premium is $165.
15) Mike is 19 years old. He uses his car for pleasure. His basic premium is $147.
16) Harry uses his car for work. He is 18 years old. His basic premium is $234.
17) Denise is 17 years old. She drives 6 miles to work. Her basic premium is $184.

Tell if the life insurance described is *term life*, *ordinary life*, *limited-payment life*, or *endowment life* insurance.

18) The policyholder pays premiums for a limited period of time. At the end of this period of time, he is paid the face amount of the policy.
19) The policyholder pays premiums for a limited period of time. He is insured only during this period.
20) The policyholder pays premiums until he dies. When he dies the beneficiary is paid the face value of the policy.

CHAPTER 16

LAWN CARE

INTRODUCTION

A *polygon* is a closed plane figure of three or more sides. As you work in your yard, you will see many polygons. The sidewalk is a long rectangle, the house might be a hexagon, the garden might be a square, and the patio might be a trapezoid.

The *perimeter* of a polygon is the measure of the distance around the polygon. You find the perimeter of a polygon by adding the lengths of its sides.

Example:

What is the perimeter of this polygon?

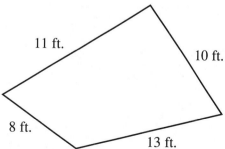

```
  13  feet
  11  feet
  10  feet
+  8  feet
  42  feet
```

The perimeter is 42 feet.

EXERCISE A.   Find the perimeter of each polygon.   Be sure that you include the unit of measure in your answer.

1)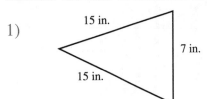

7)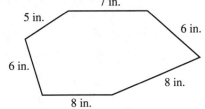

2)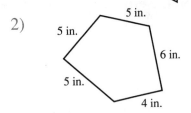

8)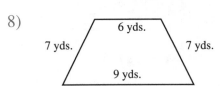

3)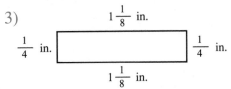

9)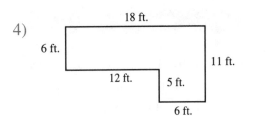

4)

10)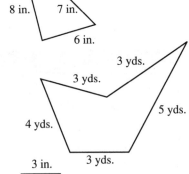

5)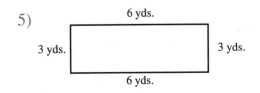

11)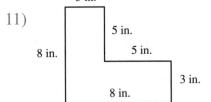

6)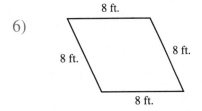

12)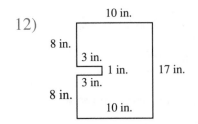

ENCLOSING YOUR YARD

One way to enclose your yard is to plant a hedge around it. To find the cost of putting a hedge around the yard, you first add the length of the sides of the area to be enclosed. You then multiply the cost of hedge per yard by this answer.

Example: Hedge costs $2.25 per yard. How much will it cost to plant a hedge around this property?

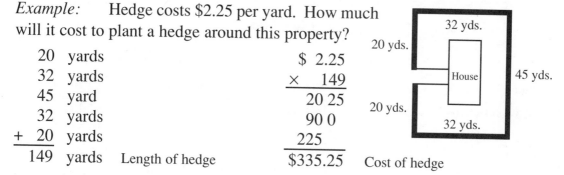

20	yards	
32	yards	
45	yard	
32	yards	
+ 20	yards	
149	yards	Length of hedge

$ 2.25
× 149
20 25
90 0
225
$335.25 Cost of hedge

EXERCISE A. Find the cost of planting a hedge along the dark lines for each property. Hedge costs $2.25 per yard. Round to the nearest cent.

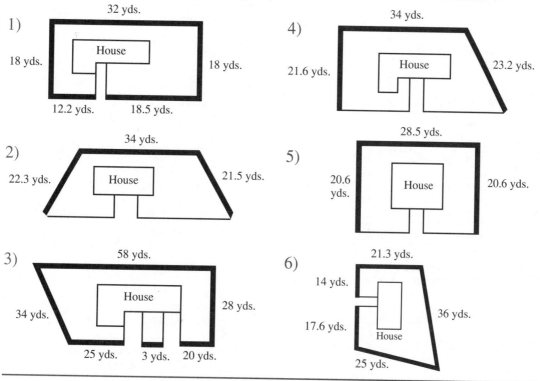

1) 32 yds. / 18 yds. / House / 18 yds. / 12.2 yds. / 18.5 yds.

2) 34 yds. / 22.3 yds. / House / 21.5 yds.

3) 58 yds. / House / 34 yds. / 28 yds. / 25 yds. / 3 yds. / 20 yds.

4) 34 yds. / 21.6 yds. / House / 23.2 yds.

5) 28.5 yds. / 20.6 yds. / House / 20.6 yds.

6) 21.3 yds. / 14 yds. / 17.6 yds. / House / 36 yds. / 25 yds.

Another way to enclose your yard is with fencing.

Example:

Find the cost of fencing in this yard. Chain link fencing costs $6.50 per yard and fence posts cost $3.75 each. Gates cost $23.35 each.

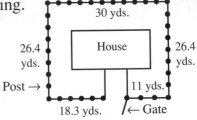

30 yds.

House

26.4 yds.

26.4 yds.

Post →

11 yds.

18.3 yds. ← Gate

Length of Fence		Cost of Fence		Total Cost
18.3	yards			
26.4	yards	112.1	$3.75	
30	yards	× $ 6.50	× 36	$728.65
26.4	yards	56 050	22 50	$135.00
+ 11	yards	672 6	112 5	+ $ 23.25
112.1	yards	$ 728.650	$ 135.00	$886.90

The total cost is $886.90.

EXERCISE B. Find the total cost of fencing in each yard.

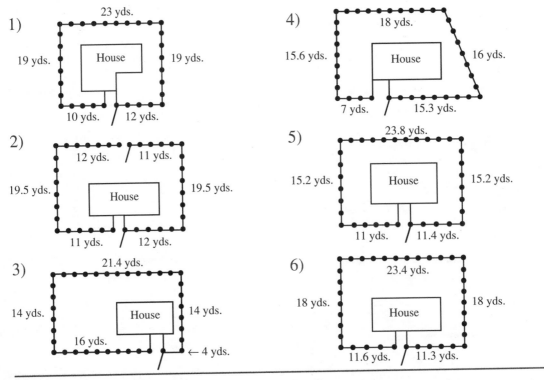

1)

23 yds.

19 yds.   House   19 yds.

10 yds. / 12 yds.

2)

12 yds. / 11 yds.

19.5 yds.   House   19.5 yds.

11 yds. / 12 yds.

3)

21.4 yds.

14 yds.   House   14 yds.

16 yds.

← 4 yds.

4)

18 yds.

15.6 yds.   House   16 yds.

7 yds. / 15.3 yds.

5)

23.8 yds.

15.2 yds.   House   15.2 yds.

11 yds. / 11.4 yds.

6)

23.4 yds.

18 yds.   House   18 yds.

11.6 yds. / 11.3 yds.

MEASURING IN INCHES

If you can measure with a ruler, you will be better able to make plans for your work in the yard. A ruler is divided into inches and each inch can be divided into 16 parts as shown below.

Example: How long is each line segment to the nearest sixteenth of an inch?

A)
B)
C)
D)
E)

INCHES   **1**   **2**   **3**   **4**   **5**

A) 2 in.   B) $1\,^3/_{16}$ in.   C) $1\,^6/_{16}$ in.   D) $2\,^4/_{16}$ in.   E) $3\,^2/_{16}$ in.

EXERCISE A. Use a ruler to find the length of each line segment to the nearest sixteenth of an inch.

1)
2)
3)
4)
5)
6)
7)
8)
9)
10)
11)
12)

USING A SCALE DRAWING

When Denise was planning her spring yard work, she made this *scale drawing*. The scale at the bottom of the drawing means that 1/16 of an inch equals 2 feet in the actual yard. Now Denise can make her plans without being outside in the yard.

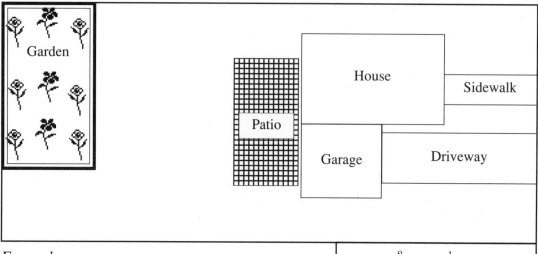

Example:

What is the actual length of the real lot?

Use a ruler and count 92 16ths.

$$\frac{1}{2 \text{ feet}} = \frac{92}{N} \quad \leftarrow \text{Number of 16ths.}$$

$$2 \times 92 = N$$

$$138 = N$$

The lot is 184 feet long.

EXERCISE A.   Find these dimensions on the real lot.

The length of the: *The width of the:*

1) house   ___   7)   lot   ___
2) garage   ___   8)   garden   ___
3) driveway   ___   9)   driveway   ___
4) sidewalk   ___   10) patio   ___
5) patio   ___   11) house   ___
6) garden   ___   12) sidewalk   ___

A R E A

Some yard work requires knowing the *area* of the yard. You find the area of a rectangle by multiplying the length by the width. Area is given in square units, like square inches (in^2) or square yards (yd^2).

Examples:

Find the area of these rectangles.

A)

$$\begin{array}{r} 13 \\ \times \quad 7 \\ \hline 91 \end{array}$$ in²

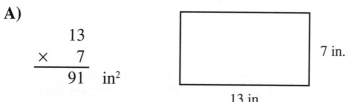

7 in.

13 in.

B)

$$\begin{array}{r} 16 \\ \times \quad 8 \\ \hline 128 \end{array}$$ ft²

$$\begin{array}{r} 12 \\ \times \quad 7 \\ \hline 84 \end{array}$$ ft²

$$\begin{array}{r} 128 \\ + \quad 84 \\ \hline 212 \end{array}$$ ft²

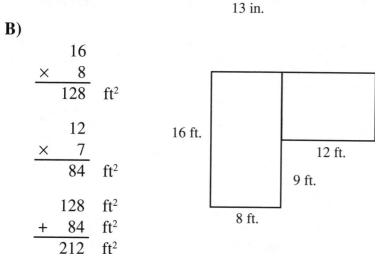

16 ft.

12 ft.

9 ft.

8 ft.

251

EXERCISE A.   Find the area of each shape.

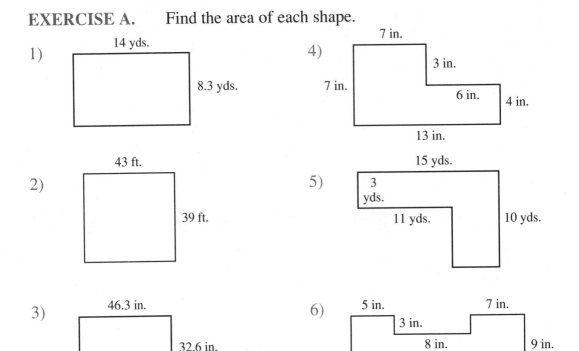

1)   14 yds.   8.3 yds.

2)   43 ft.   39 ft.

3)   46.3 in.   32.6 in.

4)   7 in.   3 in.   7 in.   6 in.   4 in.   13 in.

5)   15 yds.   3 yds.   11 yds.   10 yds.

6)   5 in.   7 in.   3 in.   8 in.   9 in.   20 in.

FERTILIZING YOUR YARD

Many people apply fertilizer to their lawn to make the grass grow better. If you apply too much, it may kill the grass. For the best results, you should use 5 lbs. of fertilizer per 200 square feet of lawn. To find the number of square feet of lawn, follow these steps:

1)   Find the total area of the lot.
2)   Find the area of any areas that are not to be fertilized.
3)   Subtract to find the area of the lawn.

Once you have found the area of the lawn, you divide by 200 to determine the number of 5-lb. bags needed. Round to the nearest whole number.

Example:

Find the amount of fertilizer that you need for this lawn.

```
        65 ft.
   ┌──────────────┐
   │ 24 ┌──────┐  │
   │ ft.│House │  │ 60 ft.
   │    └──────┘  │
   │     32 ft.   │
   └──────────────┘
```

Area of Lot	Area of House	Area of Lawn	Amount of Fertilizer
65 feet × 60 feet —————— 3900 sq. feet	32 × 24 ———— 128 64 ———— 768 sq. feet	3900 - 768 ———— 3132 sq. feet	15.6 200) 3132.0 200 ———— 1132 1000 ———— 130 0 120 0

16 bags of fertilizer will be needed for this lawn.

EXERCISE A. Find the amount of fertilizer that you need to fertilize the shaded area of each lot.

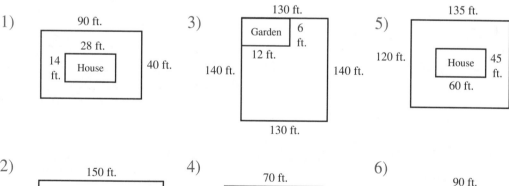

1)
90 ft.
28 ft.
14 ft.
House
40 ft.

3)
130 ft.
Garden
6 ft.
12 ft.
140 ft.
140 ft.
130 ft.

5)
135 ft.
120 ft.
House
45 ft.
60 ft.

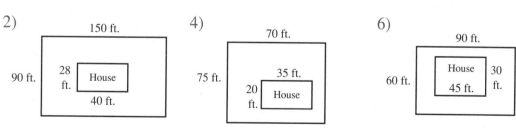

2)
150 ft.
90 ft.
28 ft.
House
40 ft.

4)
70 ft.
75 ft.
35 ft.
20 ft.
House

6)
90 ft.
60 ft.
House
45 ft.
30 ft.

VOLUME

For some jobs you will need to know the *volume* of a shape. Volume is given in cubic units, like cubic feet (ft³) or cubic yards (yd³). You find the volume of a *rectangular prism* by multiplying the length times the width times the height, or depth.

Volume	=	l × w × h
	=	4 × 2 × 3
	=	24 yd³
Length	=	4 yds.
Width	=	2 yds.
Height	=	3 yds.

1 row of 4 yd³ (4)   2 rows of 4 yd³ (4 × 2)   3 layers of 8 yd³ (4 × 2 × 3)

EXERCISE A.   Find the volume of each rectangular prism.

1)
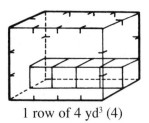
3 yds.
8 yds.
6 yds.

5)
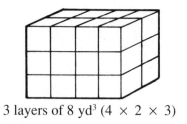
70 in.
103 in.
83 in.

2)
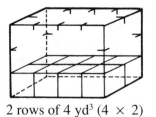
9 yds.
16 yds.
12 yds.

6)
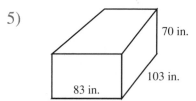
2 ft.
12 ft.
16 ft.

3)
4.6 ft.
18 ft.
23 ft.

7)
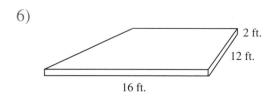
$\frac{1}{2}$ ft.
21 ft.
23.4 ft.

4)
1 ft.
16 ft.
12 ft.

8)
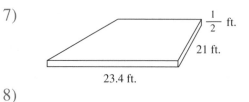
$\frac{1}{2}$ yd.
12 yds.
8 yds.

CONCRETE

You may use concrete in some yard projects, such as installing a patio or replacing a driveway or sidewalk. Concrete is ordered by the cubic yard. You can find the number of cubic yards of concrete that you will need by finding the volume of the space that is to be filled with concrete.

Example:

How much concrete will you need to replace a sidewalk that is 18 yards long and 2 yards wide? The sidewalk is to be 4 inches thick. Round up to the nearest whole number.

Express 4 inches as a yard.

$$\frac{4}{36} = \frac{1}{9}$$

$$
\begin{aligned}
V &= l \times w \times h \\
&= 18 \times 2 \times \frac{1}{9} \\
&= 4
\end{aligned}
$$

You will need 4 yards of concrete.

EXERCISE A.   Find the amount of concrete that you will need for each project. Assume 4 inches to be the thickness.

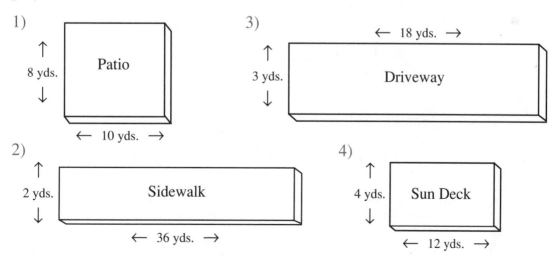

1) Patio — 8 yds. ↑↓, ← 10 yds. →

3) Driveway — 3 yds. ↑↓, ← 18 yds. →

2) Sidewalk — 2 yds. ↑↓, ← 36 yds. →

4) Sun Deck — 4 yds. ↑↓, ← 12 yds. →

EXERCISE B. Find the cost of the concrete that you will need for these projects if concrete costs $80 per cubic yard. Do not round answers.

	Project	Dimensions	Amount of Concrete	Cost of Concrete
1)	Driveway	$3 \times 48 \times \frac{1}{6}$	___	___
2)	Patio	$4 \times 6 \times \frac{1}{6}$	___	___
3)	Sidewalk	$1 \times 12 \times .1$	___	___
4)	Wall	$14 \times 21 \times .2$	___	___
5)	Sun Deck	$6 \times 5 \times \frac{1}{6}$	___	___

Calculator Practice 16

Use your calculator to help solve proportion problems.

Example: $\frac{25}{?} = \frac{5}{11}$

Step 1: Find the cross products.
Step 2: $25 \times 11 = 275$. While 275 is still on the display, divide 275 by 5. $275 \div 5 = 55$

$$\frac{25}{N} = \frac{5}{11}$$

$N \times 5 = 25 \times 11$

$N = \frac{25 \times 11}{5}$

$N = 55$

CALCULATOR EXERCISE. Use your calculator to solve these proportions.

1) $\frac{5}{16} = \frac{N}{256}$ 3) $\frac{N}{16} = \frac{7}{56}$

2) $\frac{7}{28} = \frac{N}{308}$ 4) $\frac{N}{576} = \frac{7}{18}$

Computer Practice 16

Use this program to compare ratios.

10	PRINT "COMPARING RATIOS"
20	INPUT "NUMERATOR A = ";A
30	INPUT "DENOMINATOR B = ";B
40	INPUT "NUMERATOR C = ";C
50	INPUT "DENOMINATOR D = ";D
60	IF B * D = 0 THEN 140
70	IF A/B > C/D THEN 110
80	IF A/B = C/D THEN 130
90	PRINT A;"/";B;"<";C;"/";D
100	GOTO 140
110	PRINT A;"/";B;">";C;"/";D
120	GOTO 140
130	PRINT A;"/";B;"=";C;"/";D
140	END

COMPUTER EXERCISE. Use the program to compare the following ratios.

1) $\dfrac{2}{6}$ and $\dfrac{5}{9}$

2) $\dfrac{11}{21}$ and $\dfrac{12}{13}$

3) $\dfrac{6}{11}$ and $\dfrac{9}{14}$

4) $\dfrac{16}{17}$ and $\dfrac{5}{6}$

5) $\dfrac{1}{19}$ and $\dfrac{2}{39}$

6) $\dfrac{3}{77}$ and $\dfrac{5}{105}$

Find the perimeter of each polygon.

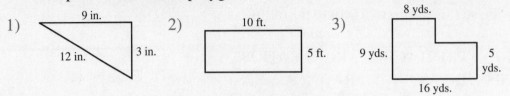

1) 9 in. 12 in. 3 in.

2) 10 ft. 5 ft.

3) 8 yds. 9 yds. 5 yds. 16 yds.

Find the cost of planting a hedge along the dark lines for each property.
Hedge costs $2.38 per yard.

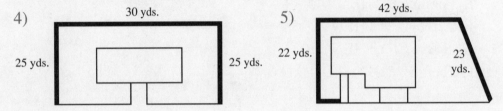

4) 30 yds. 25 yds. 25 yds.

5) 42 yds. 22 yds. 23 yds.

Measure each line segment to the nearest 1/16 of an inch.

6) ───────────────

7) ─────────────

Use your ruler and this scale drawing of a yard to answer the questions below.

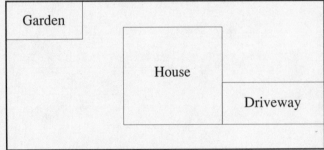

Garden

House

Driveway

Scale: 1/16 inch = 2 feet

8) What is the width of the garden?
9) What is the length of the driveway?
10) What is the width of the house?
11) What is the length of the garden?

Find the area of each polygon.

12)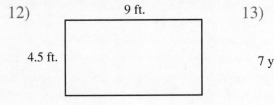
9 ft.
4.5 ft.

13)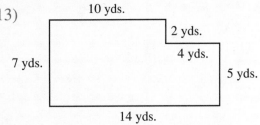
10 yds.
2 yds.
4 yds.
5 yds.
7 yds.
14 yds.

Find the number of bags of fertilizer that you would need to fertilize the shaded area of each lawn. You need a 5-lb. bag of fertilizer per 200 square feet.

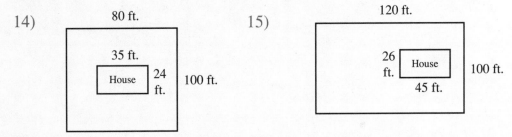

14)
80 ft.
35 ft.
House
24 ft.
100 ft.

15)
120 ft.
26 ft.
House
100 ft.
45 ft.

Find the volume of each rectangular prism.

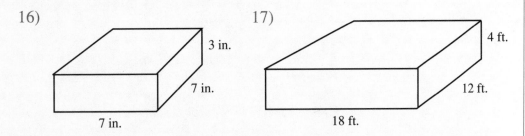

16)
3 in.
7 in.
7 in.

17)
4 ft.
12 ft.
18 ft.

Find the cost of the concrete that you will need for these projects if concrete costs $80 per cubic yard.

18) Sidewalk 1 yd. by 10 yds. by .1 yd.
19) Driveway 4 yds. by 20 yds. by .16 yds.
20) Patio 5 yds. by 8 yds. by .1 yd.

CHAPTER 17

USING ENERGY

The amount of electricity used by a household is measured in *kilowatts*. However, light bulbs and electrical appliances in the home are labeled to show their power requirements in *watts*. You need to be able to convert watts to kilowatts to understand your electric bill. Kilo means "one thousand." A kilowatt is 1,000 watts.

Example:

How many kilowatts do 3,000 watts equal?

To convert watts to kilowatts, divide the watts by 1,000.

$$
\begin{array}{r}
3 \\
1000 \overline{)\,3000} \\
3000 \\
\end{array}
$$

Answer: 3,000 watts = 3 kilowatts

There is an easier way to convert watts to kilowatts. Just move the decimal point three places to the left.

Examples:

3450 watts = 3.450 kilowatts   28 watts = .028 kilowatts

EXERCISE A.   Convert these watts to kilowatts.

1)	2000 watts	13)	39,400 watts	25)	51 watts
2)	1500 watts	14)	358 watts	26)	12.3 watts
3)	3500 watts	15)	805 watts	27)	2.63 watts
4)	4000 watts	16)	105 watts	28)	75 watts
5)	2300 watts	17)	100 watts	29)	120.3 watts
6)	1600 watts	18)	200 watts	30)	40 watts
7)	3800 watts	19)	39 watts	31)	.34 watts
8)	92,000 watts	20)	58 watts	32)	1.2 watts
9)	5305 watts	21)	80 watts	33)	5 watts
10)	60,000 watts	22)	29 watts	34)	2 watts
11)	28,000 watts	23)	64 watts	35)	4.6 watts
12)	32,100 watts	24)	913 watts	36)	1 watt

Electric companies bill their customers for the kilowatt hours of electricity they use. You can estimate the watt hours of electricity used.

For example, a 100-watt bulb that burns for 2 hours uses 200 watt hours of electricity (100 watts × 2 hours = 200 watt hours).

Two 100-watt bulbs that burn for 1 hour use 200 watts of electricity (200 watts × 1 hour = 200 watt hours).

On the other hand, three 100-watt bulbs that burn for 8 hours use 2400 watt hours of electricity (300 watts × 8 hours = 2400 watt hours).

Number of Watts × Number of Hours = Watt Hours

Example:

Margo's family used the following watts. Three 100-watt lights for 8 hours, two 150-watt lights for 3 hours, and two 75-watt lights for 4 hours. Find the total kilowatt hours they used.

Make a chart.

Number of Lamps	Watts	Hours Burned	Watt Hours
3	100	8	2400
2	150	3	900
2	75	4	600
		Total	3900
		Kilowatt hours	3.9

Explanation:

$3 \times 100 \times 8 = 2400$

$2 \times 150 \times 3 = 900$

$2 \times 75 \times 4 = 600$

EXERCISE B.   Complete the information for this chart. Convert the total watt hours to kilowatt hours.

	Number of Lamps	Watts	Hours Burned	Watt Hours
1)	3	100	6	
2)	2	75	3	
3)	1	150	4	
4)	4	200	3	
5)	6	60	4	
6)	5	25	24	
7)	3	40	8	
8)			Total	
9)			Kilowatt hours	

Reading Electric Meters. You can read your electric meter to determine the number of kilowatt hours used. Read the dials from right to left. Read the number the pointer has just passed. Take the lower number.

Example: (Start here.)

↓

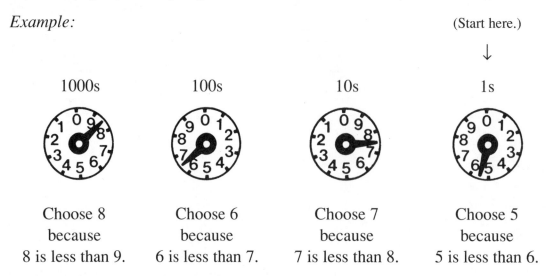

1000s	100s	10s	1s
Choose 8	Choose 6	Choose 7	Choose 5
because	because	because	because
8 is less than 9.	6 is less than 7.	7 is less than 8.	5 is less than 6.

The reading is 8675 kilowatt hours.

Even though the pointer appears to be exactly on a number, read the next lower number — unless the pointer to its right has passed zero.

Example:

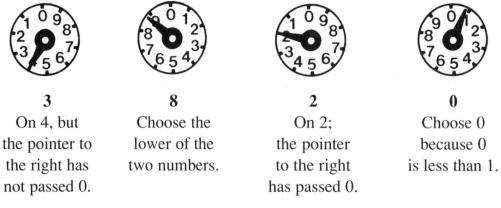

3	**8**	**2**	**0**
On 4, but the pointer to the right has not passed 0.	Choose the lower of the two numbers.	On 2; the pointer to the right has passed 0.	Choose 0 because 0 is less than 1.

The reading is 3820 kilowatt hours.

EXERCISE C.   Read the following electric meters.

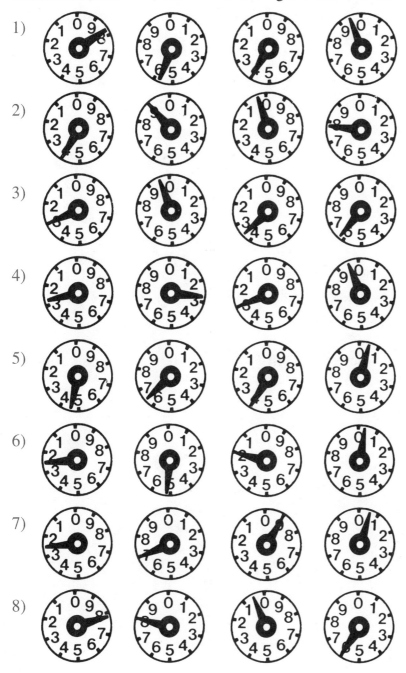

1)

2)

3)

4)

5)

6)

7)

8)

The Electric Bill. The electric company bills its customers for the number of kilowatt hours used during a billing period, which is usually one month. The cost per kilowatt hour varies from one city or area to another.

For example, Olivia's family used 1263 kilowatt hours for the month of April. Find the cost if the electric company charged 6¢ per kilowatt hour. A kilowatt hour can be expressed as kwh.

$$
\begin{array}{rl}
1263 & \text{Kilowatt hour} \\
\times \quad .06 & \text{Price per kwh} \\
\hline
\$75.78 & \text{Cost for April}
\end{array}
$$

The electric company may impose additional charges, such as fuel costs and customer service charges. The customer charge covers the expense of reading the meter and keeping account records.

For example, compute the electric bill for 1520 kwh at 5¢ with a customer charge of $2.89.

$$
\begin{array}{rl}
1520 & \text{Kwh} \\
\times \quad .05 & \text{Cost per kwh} \\
\hline
\$76.00 &
\end{array}
$$

$$
\begin{array}{rl}
\$76.00 & \\
+ \quad 2.89 & \text{Customer charge} \\
\hline
\$78.89 & \text{Total bill}
\end{array}
$$

EXERCISE D.   Compute each bill with a $2.89 customer charge.

	Kwh Used	Rate per Kwh	Total
1)	2150	6¢	___
2)	1765	5¢	___
3)	5020	7¢	___
4)	2315	7¢	___
5)	983	6¢	___
6)	1700	8¢	___
7)	671	5¢	___
8)	2175	6¢	___
9)	1008	9¢	___
10)	3114	10¢	___
11)	5102	7¢	___
12)	1192	8¢	___
13)	1983	6¢	___
14)	2032	6¢	___
15)	4452	7¢	___
16)	1001	9¢	___

Calculator Practice 17

Use your calculator to determine the number of kilowatt hours used.

CALCULATOR EXERCISE. Subtract the smaller reading from the larger.

1)	2368 to 2815	8)	6129 to 7815	15)	2963 to 4185
2)	5872 to 6023	9)	3002 to 4726	16)	8615 to 9031
3)	8211 to 9903	10)	8362 to 9108	17)	5620 to 7516
4)	4020 to 5107	11)	4554 to 6218	18)	8001 to 9532
5)	3083 to 5116	12)	2315 to 4063	19)	1316 to 2235
6)	4135 to 6102	13)	2912 to 3244	20)	2273 to 3442
7)	7319 to 8082	14)	6691 to 8354	21)	6083 to 8510

Computer Practice 17

Use a computer to determine each electric bill in the exercise above. The cost of 6¢ per kwh is written into the program. (See Appendix for more information.)

```
10    PRINT "COMPUTING THE COST FOR KILOWATT HOURS"
20    INPUT "KILOWATT HOURS = ";K
30    IF K = 0 THEN 70
40    X = .06 * K
50    PRINT "THE COST IS $";X
60    GOTO 20
70    END
```

To stop the program, type 0 for kilowatt hours.

COMPUTER EXERCISE. Change Line 40 to X = .07 * K. Compute the cost, using 7¢ per kwh, for each of the following:

1)	283 kwh	5)	1506 kwh	9)	3015 kwh
2)	1063 kwh	6)	1132 kwh	10)	3162 kwh
3)	785 kwh	7)	2635 kwh	11)	178 kwh
4)	1096 kwh	8)	4216 kwh	12)	1061 kwh

GAS

The gas meter, like the electric meter, is read from right to left. A meter may have three or four dials, but all gas and electric meters are read the same way.

502 thousand cubic feet

Gas is measured in thousands of cubic feet. However, gas customers are billed for the hundreds of cubic feet they use. You can convert the reading to hundreds of cubic feet by multiplying the meter reading by 10.

Example:

502 thousand cubic feet = 5020 hundred cubic feet because $502 \times 10 = 5020$.

EXERCISE A.   Convert each gas reading to hundreds of cubic feet.

1)   236 thousand cu. ft.
2)   400 thousand cu. ft.
3)   356 thousand cu. ft.
4)   210 thousand cu. ft.
5)   109 thousand cu. ft.
6)   3001 thousand cu. ft.
7)   291 thousand cu. ft.
8)   801 thousand cu. ft.
9)   407 thousand cu. ft.
10) 725 thousand cu. ft.
11) 4063 thousand cu. ft.
12) 4441 thousand cu. ft.
13) 268 thousand cu. ft.
14) 3399 thousand cu. ft.

15) 2912 thousand cu. ft.
16) 762 thousand cu. ft.
17) 1000 thousand cu. ft.
18) 2000 thousand cu. ft.
19) 3022 thousand cu. ft.
20) 543 thousand cu. ft.
21) 304 thousand cu. ft.
22) 1200 thousand cu. ft.
23) 206 thousand cu. ft.
24) 885 thousand cu. ft.
25) 2934 thousand cu. ft.
26) 1901 thousand cu. ft.
27) 415 thousand cu. ft.
28) 1002 thousand cu. ft.

EXERCISE B.   Read each gas meter. Convert the reading to hundreds of cubic feet.

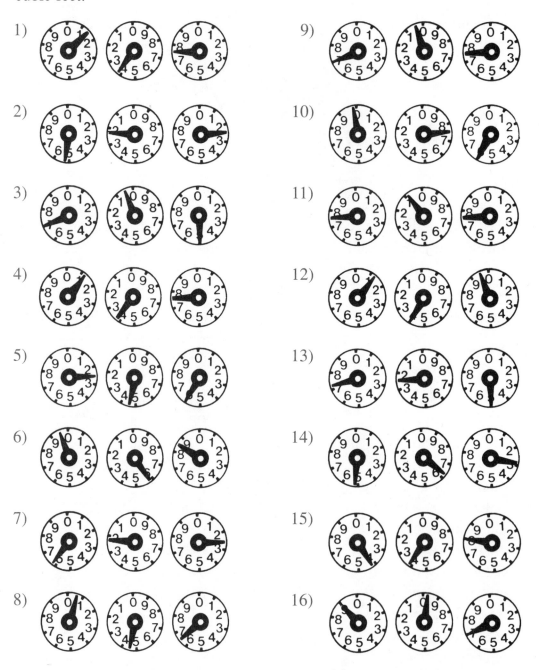

1)

2)

3)

4)

5)

6)

7)

8)

9)

10)

11)

12)

13)

14)

15)

16)

TEMPERATURE

The amount of energy you use to heat or cool your home depends on weather conditions. Furnaces and water heaters work extra hard during freezing winter temperatures. Air conditioners and fans are used more during hot summer days.

Converting Celsius Readings to Fahrenheit. Temperatures may be reported in Celsius readings.

30° C is the same as 86° F.

To convert Celsius to Fahrenheit, use this formula:

$$F = \frac{9}{5} \times C + 32$$

Fahrenheit temperature   Celsius temperature

Examples:

Convert 25° Celsius to Fahrenheit.

$$\text{Use} \quad F = \frac{9}{5} \times C + 32$$
$$F = \frac{9}{5} \times 25 + 32$$
$$F = 45 + 32$$
$$F = 77°$$

Convert 26° Celsius to Fahrenheit.

$$\text{Use} \quad F = \frac{9}{5} \times C + 32$$
$$F = \frac{9}{5} \times 26 + 32$$
$$F = 46\frac{4}{5} + 32$$
$$F = 78\frac{4}{5}°$$

Converting Fahrenheit Readings to Celsius. To convert a Fahrenheit reading to Celsius, use this formula:

$$C = \frac{5}{9} \times (F - 32)$$

Celsius   Fahrenheit
temperature   temperature

Examples:

Convert 75° Fahrenheit to Celsius.

$$C = \frac{5}{9} \times (F - 32)$$

$$C = \frac{5}{9} \times (75 - 32)$$

$$C = \frac{5}{9} \times 43$$

$$C \times 23\frac{8}{9}°$$

Convert 80° Fahrenheit to Celsius.

$$C = \frac{5}{9} \times (80 - 32)$$

$$C = \frac{5}{9} \times 48$$

$$C = 26\frac{2}{3}°$$

EXERCISE A.   Convert the following Celsius temperatures to Fahrenheit.

1) 25°

2) 30°

3) 60°

4) 15°

5) 55°

6) 36°

7) 42°

8) 45°

9) 20°

10) 53°

11) 18°

12) 23°

EXERCISE B.   Convert the following Fahrenheit temperatures to Celsius.

1) 68°

2) 50°

3) 122°

4) 104°

5) 32°

6) 80°

7) 62°

8) 35°

9) 44°

10) 98°

11) 72°

12) 85°

Convert to kilowatts.

1) 2639 watts

2) 37 watts

Choose the correct answer.

3) 700 watts burning for 5 hours equals:
   a) 35 kwh
   b) .35 kwh
   c) 3.5 kwh
   d) 3500 kwh

Read this electric meter.

4)

Answer these questions.

5) What are the charges for 2367 kwh used at 7¢ per kwh?

6) What is the bill for 3076 kwh used at 8¢ per kwh, with an added fuel cost of $15.16?

7) How many hundred cubic feet are equal to 28 thousand cubic feet?

8) What is 11° C converted to Fahrenheit?

9) What is 65° F converted to Celsius?

Read this gas meter.

10)

SUPPLEMENTARY
PROBLEMS

R E V I E W   O F   B A S I C   S K I L L S   1

Identifying the Place Value of Whole Numbers

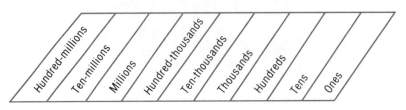

Example: Write the name of the place of the underlined digit.

65823   thousands

2906   tens

4790098   millions

EXERCISE: Write the name of the place for each underlined digit.

1) 23,456
2) 536
3) 5126
4) 621
5) 150,341
6) 780,296
7) 3,103,615
8) 82,605
9) 26
10) 7405
11) 41,811
12) 963
13) 31,005
14) 1815
15) 1007
16) 81,001
17) 567
18) 314,152
19) 72,855
20) 6,293,000

Rounding Whole Numbers

To the nearer ten:	**Step 1:** Find the place to be rounded.	To the nearer hundred:
582 ↑ tens		68154 ↑ hundreds
582 ↑	**Step 2:** If the digit to the right is 5 or more, add 1 to the place to be rounded.	68154 ↑
580	**Step 3:** Change all digits to the right of the rounded place to zeros.	68200

EXERCISE: Round these numbers to the nearest:

		Ten	Hundred	Thousand
1)	26311	_____	_____	_____
2)	40592	_____	_____	_____
3)	7098	_____	_____	_____
4)	415	_____	_____	_____
5)	89	_____	_____	_____
6)	49	_____	_____	_____
7)	2900	_____	_____	_____
8)	3200	_____	_____	_____
9)	4	_____	_____	_____
10)	129	_____	_____	_____

REVIEW OF BASIC SKILLS 3

Adding Whole Numbers

Example: 26 + 451 + 2 =

Solution:
$$\begin{array}{r} 26 \\ 451 \quad \leftarrow \text{Addends} \\ +\ \ 2 \\ \hline 479 \quad \leftarrow \text{Sum or total} \end{array}$$

Example: 7 + 0 =

Solution:
$$\begin{array}{r} 7 \quad \leftarrow \text{Addend} \\ +\ \ 0 \quad \leftarrow \text{Addend} \\ \hline 7 \quad \leftarrow \text{Sum or total} \end{array}$$

EXERCISE: Write these addends in vertical form. Then add.

1)	235 + 62	19)	45 + 671
2)	503 + 263	20)	215 + 823
3)	211 + 623	21)	305 + 876
4)	26 + 78 + 9	22)	516 + 23 + 8
5)	395 + 75 + 37	23)	3007 + 926 + 85
6)	314 + 625 + 893	24)	27 + 851 + 623
7)	512 + 726 + 89	25)	351 + 603 + 1151
8)	1033 + 78 + 201	26)	403 + 1151 + 69
9)	1515 + 301 + 201	27)	62 + 89 + 5 + 301
10)	51 + 8992 + 7	28)	702 + 98 + 304
11)	72 + 6203 + 45	29)	1346 + 62 + 891
12)	10638 + 2957	30)	29063 + 29 + 305
13)	6203 + 89 + 1458	31)	62301 + 89 + 901
14)	1502 + 84 + 201	32)	375 + 1002 + 962
15)	302 + 895 + 102	33)	1302 + 63 + 115
16)	4403 + 789 + 62	34)	463 + 891 + 200
17)	5067 + 29835	35)	135 + 60039 + 12
18)	26 + 2419 + 231	36)	48 + 121 + 2635

Subtracting Whole Numbers

Example: Subtract 26 from 235. The number following "from" is written first.

Solution:
```
    235    Minuend
  -  26    Subtrahend
    209    Difference
```

Check:
```
     26
  + 209
    235
```

EXERCISE: Write these problems vertically. Then subtract.

1)	208 - 45 =		23)	400 - 28 =
2)	351 - 290 =		24)	614 - 326 =
3)	265 - 28 =		25)	3105 - 106 =
4)	208 - 177 =		26)	4992 - 885 =
5)	1066 - 815 =		27)	3001 - 223 =
6)	1210 - 986 =		28)	8191 - 310 =
7)	6213 - 866 =		29)	3355 - 2665 =
8)	7019 - 669 =		30)	3274 - 2275 =
9)	5287 - 2008 =		31)	8101 - 4283 =
10)	1010 - 935 =		32)	9000 - 862 =
11)	37,115 - 235 =		33)	2113 - 421 =
12)	5351 - 709 =		34)	48,300 - 9,301 =
13)	17,315 - 9115 =		35)	41,041 - 8,597 =
14)	20,061 - 4805 =		36)	14,724 - 7,026 =
15)	30,155 - 7132 =		37)	65,913 - 27,261 =
16)	23,103 - 9163 =		38)	10,991 - 2815 =
17)	50,167 - 12,735 =		39)	41,568 - 29,321 =
18)	37,451 - 16,203 =		40)	20,972 - 3811 =
19)	81,131 - 17,788 =		41)	10,014 - 2560 =
20)	16,683 - 6891 =		42)	57,221 - 10,811 =
21)	55,103 - 2317 =		43)	51,371 - 5119 =
22)	88,471 - 73,115 =		44)	14,014 - 7958 =

Multiplying Whole Numbers (5)

Example: $23 \times 6 =$

Solution:

$$
\begin{array}{r}
23 \\
\times \quad 6 \\
\hline
138 \\
\end{array}
$$
Factors
Product

Example: $46 \times 35 =$

$$
\begin{array}{r}
46 \\
\times \quad 35 \\
\hline
230 \\
138 \\
\hline
1610 \\
\end{array}
$$
Factors

Product

Multiplying Whole Numbers with Zeros (6)

Example: 267×10 ← One zero

Solution:

$$
\begin{array}{r}
267 \\
\times \quad 10 \\
\hline
2670 \\
\end{array}
$$
← One zero

Example: 342×100 ← Two zeros

$$
\begin{array}{r}
342 \\
\times \quad 100 \\
\hline
34200 \\
\end{array}
$$
← Two zeros

EXERCISE: Write these problems in vertical form. Then multiply.

1) $23 \times 6 =$

2) $403 \times 5 =$

3) $313 \times 4 =$

4) $26 \times 45 =$

5) $72 \times 35 =$

6) $567 \times 10 =$

7) $109 \times 50 =$

8) $815 \times 400 =$

9) $701 \times 202 =$

10) $511 \times 120 =$

11) $2215 \times 63 =$

12) $6057 \times 40 =$

13) $5063 \times 41 =$

14) $2267 \times 19 =$

15) $2830 \times 110 =$

16) $5011 \times 300 =$

17) $7706 \times 250 =$

18) $1127 \times 277 =$

19) $90681 \times 22 =$

20) $15012 \times 50 =$

21) $21305 \times 100 =$

22) $89000 \times 62 =$

23) $4805 \times 1001 =$

24) $57119 \times 1010 =$

25) $77805 \times 601 =$

26) $38 \times 9 =$

27) $206 \times 8 =$

28) $231 \times 11 =$

29) $52 \times 60 =$

30) $391 \times 20 =$

31) $435 \times 39 =$

32) $623 \times 67 =$

33) $516 \times 200 =$

34) $870 \times 270 =$

35) $603 \times 250 =$

36) $4120 \times 10 =$

37) $1403 \times 27 =$

38) $8010 \times 50 =$

39) $3115 \times 28 =$

40) $4100 \times 310 =$

41) $8214 \times 200 =$

42) $5066 \times 305 =$

43) $6405 \times 115 =$

44) $40363 \times 100 =$

45) $71106 \times 602 =$

46) $28015 \times 101 =$

47) $10376 \times 203 =$

48) $72011 \times 78 =$

49) $90301 \times 201 =$

50) $53103 \times 111 =$

Dividing Whole Numbers with Zeros (7)

Example: $576 \div 12$

Solution:

$$\begin{array}{r} 48 \\ 12\overline{)576} \\ 48 \\ \hline 96 \\ 96 \\ \hline 00 \end{array}$$

Check:

$$\begin{array}{r} 48 \\ \times\ 12 \\ \hline 96 \\ 48 \\ \hline 576 \end{array}$$

Dividing Whole Numbers with Fractional Remainders (8)

Example: $3191 \div 25$

Solution:

$$127\frac{16}{25}$$
$$\begin{array}{r} 25\overline{)3191} \\ 25 \\ \hline 69 \\ 50 \\ \hline 191 \\ 175 \\ \hline 16 \end{array}$$

Write the remainder over the divisor

Check:

$$\begin{array}{r} 127 \\ \times\ 25 \\ \hline 635 \\ 254 \\ \hline 3175 \\ +\quad 16 \\ \hline 3191 \end{array}$$ Remainder

Dividing Whole Numbers with Zeros in the Quotient (9)

Example: $2380 \div 14$

Solution:

$$\begin{array}{r} 170 \\ 14\overline{)2380} \\ 14 \\ \hline 98 \\ 98 \\ \hline 00 \end{array}$$

Check:

$$\begin{array}{r} 170 \\ \times\ 14 \\ \hline 680 \\ 170 \\ \hline 2380 \end{array}$$

Example: $4864 \div 16$

Solution:

$$\begin{array}{r} 304 \\ 16\overline{)4864} \\ 48 \\ \hline 064 \\ 64 \end{array}$$

Check:

$$\begin{array}{r} 304 \\ \times\ 16 \\ \hline 1824 \\ 304 \\ \hline 4864 \end{array}$$

EXERCISE: Copy these problems and divide.

1)	$138 \div 6 =$	26)	$371 \div 7 =$
2)	$882 \div 9 =$	27)	$3159 \div 9 =$
3)	$1030 \div 5 =$	28)	$1744 \div 8 =$
4)	$1806 \div 6 =$	29)	$3018 \div 6 =$
5)	$1631 \div 7 =$	30)	$2564 \div 4 =$
6)	$3060 \div 4 =$	31)	$6033 \div 3 =$
7)	$1404 \div 52 =$	32)	$1539 \div 27 =$
8)	$4980 \div 60 =$	33)	$4100 \div 82 =$
9)	$5040 \div 70 =$	34)	$8820 \div 90 =$
10)	$5700 \div 95 =$	35)	$3375 \div 25 =$
11)	$6510 \div 105 =$	36)	$3450 \div 15 =$
12)	$9108 \div 18 =$	37)	$19418 \div 38 =$
13)	$30954 \div 77 =$	38)	$31626 \div 63 =$
14)	$15257 \div 73 =$	39)	$19530 \div 62 =$
15)	$9646 \div 91 =$	40)	$10160 \div 80 =$
16)	$19520 \div 32 =$	41)	$34310 \div 47 =$
17)	$30310 \div 70 =$	42)	$52920 \div 60 =$
18)	$32040 \div 40 =$	43)	$8866 \div 22 =$
19)	$45150 \div 15 =$	44)	$138253 \div 23 =$
20)	$56221 \div 11 =$	45)	$738500 \div 35 =$
21)	$44520 \div 12 =$	46)	$50300 \div 10 =$
22)	$65160 \div 36 =$	47)	$103200 \div 24 =$
23)	$51090 \div 13 =$	48)	$82212 \div 51 =$
24)	$80080 \div 40 =$	49)	$90900 \div 30 =$
25)	$12524 \div 31 =$	50)	$57414 \div 14 =$

SUPPLEMENTARY PROBLEMS

EXERCISE: Copy these problems and divide. Write any remainders as fractions.

1)	$335 \div 6 =$	26)	$573 \div 6 =$
2)	$50 \div 8 =$	27)	$908 \div 9 =$
3)	$711 \div 9 =$	28)	$630 \div 9 =$
4)	$393 \div 6 =$	29)	$721 \div 8 =$
5)	$7151 \div 8 =$	30)	$3900 \div 9 =$
6)	$6205 \div 15 =$	31)	$8003 \div 15 =$
7)	$60600 \div 15 =$	32)	$7440 \div 22 =$
8)	$181819 \div 18 =$	33)	$32331 \div 16 =$
9)	$30091 \div 25 =$	34)	$7910 \div 19 =$
10)	$70111 \div 80 =$	35)	$51631 \div 25 =$
11)	$41015 \div 32 =$	36)	$10631 \div 81 =$
12)	$26031 \div 26 =$	37)	$35103 \div 34 =$
13)	$13315 \div 25 =$	38)	$14401 \div 72 =$
14)	$60031 \div 81 =$	39)	$42002 \div 60 =$
15)	$53010 \div 52 =$	40)	$73106 \div 73 =$
16)	$10008 \div 50 =$	41)	$53010 \div 38 =$
17)	$27023 \div 62 =$	42)	$14108 \div 80 =$
18)	$15132 \div 25 =$	43)	$62031 \div 20 =$
19)	$90615 \div 23 =$	44)	$72150 \div 80 =$
20)	$46023 \div 23 =$	45)	$81035 \div 90 =$
21)	$23310 \div 70 =$	46)	$34210 \div 81 =$
22)	$50003 \div 85 =$	47)	$78311 \div 30 =$
23)	$22022 \div 60 =$	48)	$37101 \div 51 =$
24)	$463201 \div 71 =$	49)	$72101 \div 82 =$
25)	$57231 \div 500 =$	50)	$80031 \div 198 =$

Finding Values of Numbers with Exponents

Example: Find 3^4.
Solution: $3^4 = 3 \times 3 \times 3 \times 3$ (4 times)
$= 81$

Example: Find 2^3.
Solution: $2^3 = 2 \times 2 \times 2$ (3 times)
$= 8$

EXERCISE: Write the value of each expression.

1)	3^2 =	26)	4^3 =	51)	5^2 =
2)	5^3 =	27)	4^2 =	52)	8^2 =
3)	9^2 =	28)	2^5 =	53)	9^3 =
4)	19^2 =	29)	7^3 =	54)	4^5 =
5)	3^5 =	30)	2^4 =	55)	6^2 =
6)	8^2 =	31)	11^2 =	56)	13^3 =
7)	9^4 =	32)	16^3 =	57)	12^2 =
8)	18^2 =	33)	5^4 =	58)	18^2 =
9)	6^3 =	34)	10^4 =	59)	28^2 =
10)	2^6 =	35)	15^2 =	60)	17^2 =
11)	25^2 =	36)	5^5 =	61)	24^2 =
12)	7^2 =	37)	8^4 =	62)	150^2 =
13)	2^7 =	38)	50^3 =	63)	300^4 =
14)	26^2 =	39)	5^3 =	64)	70^3 =
15)	7^4 =	40)	40^3 =	65)	22^2 =
16)	30^2 =	41)	77^2 =	66)	500^3 =
17)	200^3 =	42)	60^3 =	67)	15^3 =
18)	70^2 =	43)	92^2 =	68)	13^2 =
19)	100^3 =	44)	30^3 =	69)	42^2 =
20)	80^3 =	45)	80^2 =	70)	90^3 =
21)	30^4 =	46)	32^2 =	71)	10^3 =
22)	1000^2 =	47)	16^2 =	72)	30^4 =
23)	46^2 =	48)	10^2 =	73)	63^2 =
24)	5^6 =	49)	8^3 =	74)	10^5 =
25)	10^4 =	50)	23^2 =	75)	3^3 =

R E V I E W   O F   B A S I C   S K I L L S   1 1

Using the Order of Operations (Fundamental)

Rules:
1) Evaluate expressions with exponents first.
2) Multiply and divide from left to right in order.
3) Add and subtract from left to right in order.

Example: $\quad 2 \quad + \quad 3 \times 4 \quad - \quad 8 \div 4$

Solution: $\quad 2 \quad + \quad 3 \times 4 \quad - \quad 8 \div 4 \quad =$

$$2 \quad + \quad 12 \quad - \quad 2 \quad = \quad 12$$

Example: $\quad 2^3 \quad + \quad 3 \times 4 \div 2 \quad - \quad 48 \div 4^2 \quad =$

$$8 \quad + \quad 3 \times 4 \div 2 \quad - \quad 48 \div 16$$

$$12 \div 2 \qquad 3$$

$$8 \quad + \quad 6 \quad - \quad 3 \quad = \quad 11$$

EXERCISE: Use the rules for the order of operations. Find the answers.

1) $3 + 8 \times 2 \div 4 =$

2) $5 + 9 \times 4 \div 12 - 2 =$

3) $8 - 8 \div 4 + 3 \times 2 =$

4) $13 - 16 \times 3 \div 12 - 1 =$

5) $9 + 6 \times 3 - 8 \times 2 \div 4 =$

6) $1 + 16 \times 3 \div 12 - 4 =$

7) $14 + 32 \div 16 - 4 \times 2 =$

8) $32 \div 16 + 9 \div 3 \times 2 =$

9) $5 - 16 \div 4 + 1 + 3 =$

10) $35 - 25 \times 4 \div 20 + 5 =$

11) $2^3 + 8 \times 2^2 + 3 =$

12) $8 - 6^2 \div 12 + 2 \times 5 =$

13) $15 + 8^2 \div 4 - 6 =$

14) $26 + 13^2 \div 13 - 20 =$

15) $9^2 + 32 \div 8 \times 4 - 6 =$

16) $3 + 2^3 \div 2^2 - 4 =$

17) $5 + 8 \times 9 \div 6^2 - 4 =$

18) $25 + 11^2 + 8 \times 2 - 3 =$

19) $39 \div 13 + 12^2 \div 6 - 5 =$

20) $52 + 12 \div 2^2 - 82 \div 2 + 3^2 =$

21) $35 + 2^5 \div 2^4 \times 3^2 - 2^3 =$

22) $18 \div 3^2 + 6 \times 8 \div 4^2 - 5 =$

23) $4 \times 3 \times 5 \div 10 + 8 \times 2^3 \div 2^4 =$

24) $9 - 16 \times 3 \div 12 + 8 \div 2^2 - 2^2 =$

Finding an Average

Example: Find the average for 98, 88, and 80.

Solution: Add the numbers. Divide the sum by the number of addends.

$$
\begin{array}{r}
98 \\
88 \\
+\ 80 \\
\hline
266 \quad \text{3 addends}
\end{array}
$$

$$
\begin{array}{r}
88\frac{2}{3} \\
3\overline{)266} \\
24 \\
\hline
26 \\
24 \\
\hline
2
\end{array}
$$

Answer: The average is $88\frac{2}{3}$.

EXERCISE: Compute the averages for each set of numbers.

1)   25, 63, 48, 52, 49, 38, 42, 67, 38

2)   98, 53, 42, 56, 72, 36, 72

3)   39, 40, 39, 62, 53, 86, 29, 34

4)   95, 83, 39, 42, 88, 77, 75, 42, 67

5)   88, 62, 42, 53, 96, 35, 35

6)   53, 60, 72, 43, 35, 39, 53

7)   52, 65, 83, 96, 35, 100, 92, 53

8)   91, 62, 39, 50, 42, 88, 53, 60, 83, 72

9)   36, 50, 42, 53, 46, 82, 80, 50, 52, 39

10)   81, 90, 92, 90, 83, 43, 46, 72, 53

11)   100, 103, 96, 105, 105, 97, 102, 120

12)   36, 42, 85, 92, 30, 33, 88, 29, 62, 50

13)   109, 156, 95, 108, 90, 83, 45, 80, 90, 98, 93, 96

14)   40, 42, 43, 40, 41, 42, 43, 48, 44, 42, 45, 42

15)   40, 38, 37, 35, 42, 43, 36, 49, 48, 53, 42, 39, 34

16)   21, 20, 23, 28, 25, 23, 20, 25, 24, 29, 28, 24, 22, 20

17)   52, 50, 59, 62, 63, 55, 54, 58, 60, 50, 52, 53, 57, 52, 51

18)   56, 50, 53, 65, 73, 72, 80, 95, 81, 87, 70, 82, 96, 68

19)   23, 12, 94, 71, 44, 39, 62, 57, 68, 25, 53, 22, 19, 80

SUPPLEMENTARY PROBLEMS

REVIEW OF BASIC SKILLS 13-14

Comparing Fractions (13)

Example: Compare $\frac{3}{4}$ and $\frac{5}{8}$.

Solution:

$24 \quad \frac{3}{4} \quad\times\quad \frac{5}{8} \quad 20$

Because   Because
$4 \times 5 = 20$ $3 \times 8 = 24$

24 is greater than 20; therefore, $\frac{3}{4}$ is greater than $\frac{5}{8}$.

Changing Fractions to Higher Terms (14)

Example: Write $\frac{5}{6}$ as a fraction with 30 as the new denominator.

Solution: **Step 1:** $\frac{5}{6} = \frac{?}{30}$

Step 2: Divide 30 by 6. → $6 \overline{)30}^{\,5}$

Step 3: Multiply $\frac{5}{6}$ by $\frac{5}{5}$. → $\frac{5 \times 5}{6 \times 5} = \frac{25}{30}$

Answer: $\frac{5}{6} = \frac{25}{30}$.

EXERCISE: Express these fractions in higher terms.

1) $\frac{3}{4} = \frac{}{48}$

2) $\frac{1}{3} = \frac{}{21}$

3) $\frac{2}{3} = \frac{}{15}$

4) $\frac{5}{6} = \frac{}{18}$

5) $\frac{7}{8} = \frac{}{56}$

6) $\frac{3}{5} = \frac{}{20}$

7) $\frac{1}{7} = \frac{}{49}$

8) $\frac{5}{12} = \frac{}{24}$

9) $\frac{3}{7} = \frac{}{21}$

10) $\frac{4}{12} = \frac{}{36}$

11) $\frac{4}{9} = \frac{}{45}$

12) $\frac{3}{3} = \frac{}{18}$

13) $\frac{2}{11} = \frac{}{121}$

14) $\frac{15}{16} = \frac{}{48}$

15) $\frac{3}{10} = \frac{}{30}$

16) $\frac{12}{14} = \frac{}{70}$

17) $\frac{9}{12} = \frac{}{144}$

18) $\frac{5}{15} = \frac{}{45}$

19) $\frac{2}{8} = \frac{}{96}$

20) $\frac{1}{6} = \frac{}{72}$

21) $\frac{17}{24} = \frac{}{120}$

Renaming Fractions to Simplest Terms

Example: Rename $\dfrac{14}{16}$ to simplest terms.

Solution: $\dfrac{14 \div 2}{16 \div 2} = \dfrac{7}{8}$

Choose a number that can be divided into the denominator and the numerator.

Example: Rename $\dfrac{24}{30}$ to simplest terms.

Solution: $\dfrac{24 \div 3}{30 \div 3} = \dfrac{8}{10}$

The division process may occur more than once if the divisor is not large enough in the first step. $\dfrac{8 \div 2}{10 \div 2} = \dfrac{4}{5}$

Answer: $\dfrac{24}{30} = \dfrac{4}{5}$

EXERCISE: Rename these fractions in simplest terms.

1) $\dfrac{24}{48} =$

2) $\dfrac{10}{230} =$

3) $\dfrac{45}{99} =$

4) $\dfrac{5}{25} =$

5) $\dfrac{13}{39} =$

6) $\dfrac{56}{58} =$

7) $\dfrac{63}{81} =$

8) $\dfrac{6}{54} =$

9) $\dfrac{16}{112} =$

10) $\dfrac{39}{52} =$

11) $\dfrac{12}{60} =$

12) $\dfrac{16}{64} =$

13) $\dfrac{18}{36} =$

14) $\dfrac{22}{121} =$

15) $\dfrac{53}{106} =$

16) $\dfrac{18}{72} =$

17) $\dfrac{5}{15} =$

18) $\dfrac{55}{242} =$

19) $\dfrac{10}{52} =$

20) $\dfrac{48}{96} =$

21) $\dfrac{28}{56} =$

Renaming Improper Fractions as Mixed Numbers or Whole Numbers (16)

Example: Rename $\dfrac{13}{5}$.

Solution: Divide the numerator by the denominator.

$$
\begin{array}{r}
2 \\
5\,\overline{)\,13} \\
\underline{10} \\
3
\end{array}
\quad \leftarrow \text{Remainder}
$$

Answer: $\dfrac{13}{5} = 2\dfrac{3}{5}$ $\leftarrow$ Write the remainder over the divisor.

Example: Rename $\dfrac{42}{16}$.

Solution:

$$
\begin{array}{r}
2 \\
16\,\overline{)\,42} \\
\underline{32} \\
10
\end{array}
$$

$$2\dfrac{10}{16} = 2\dfrac{5}{8}$$

Answer: $\dfrac{42}{16} = 2\dfrac{5}{8}$

Writing Mixed Numbers in Simplest Terms (17)

Example: Write $12\dfrac{4}{6}$ in simplest terms.

Solution: $12\dfrac{4}{6} = 12 + \dfrac{4}{6} = 12 + \dfrac{2}{3} = 12\dfrac{2}{3}$

Answer: $12\dfrac{4}{6} = 12\dfrac{2}{3}$

EXERCISE: Rename these improper fractions as either mixed numbers or whole numbers.

1) $\dfrac{13}{5} =$

2) $\dfrac{18}{3} =$

3) $\dfrac{19}{6} =$

4) $\dfrac{14}{3} =$

5) $\dfrac{23}{4} =$

6) $\dfrac{12}{2} =$

7) $\dfrac{38}{5} =$

8) $\dfrac{66}{11} =$

9) $\dfrac{56}{11} =$

10) $\dfrac{19}{5} =$

11) $\dfrac{52}{32} =$

12) $\dfrac{55}{8} =$

13) $\dfrac{28}{6} =$

14) $\dfrac{32}{4} =$

15) $\dfrac{90}{3} =$

16) $\dfrac{63}{8} =$

17) $\dfrac{50}{6} =$

18) $\dfrac{58}{7} =$

19) $\dfrac{52}{10} =$

20) $\dfrac{37}{3} =$

21) $\dfrac{120}{10} =$

22) $\dfrac{73}{8} =$

23) $\dfrac{13}{2} =$

24) $\dfrac{51}{4} =$

25) $\dfrac{82}{9} =$

26) $\dfrac{23}{5} =$

27) $\dfrac{52}{8} =$

28) $\dfrac{32}{15} =$

Renaming Mixed Numbers as Improper Fractions

Example: Write $2\frac{3}{4}$ as an improper fraction.

Solution: **Step 1:**   Multiply the whole number by the denominator.
$2 \times 4 = 8$

Step 2:   Add the numerator to the product from Step 1.
$3 + 8 = 11$

Step 3:   Write the sum over the old denominator.

$$\frac{11}{8}$$

Answer: $2\frac{3}{4} = \frac{11}{8}$

EXERCISE: Rename these mixed numbers as improper fractions.

1) $3\frac{2}{5} =$

2) $6\frac{2}{5} =$

3) $5\frac{1}{6} =$

4) $7\frac{2}{12} =$

5) $2\frac{1}{6} =$

6) $9\frac{1}{2} =$

7) $4\frac{1}{9} =$

8) $8\frac{2}{11} =$

9) $5\frac{2}{3} =$

10) $8\frac{1}{3} =$

11) $6\frac{10}{13} =$

12) $16\frac{2}{3} =$

13) $7\frac{3}{8} =$

14) $15\frac{2}{3} =$

15) $13\frac{9}{14} =$

16) $9\frac{2}{3} =$

17) $5\frac{11}{10} =$

18) $20\frac{2}{3} =$

19) $16\frac{5}{21} =$

20) $11\frac{1}{8} =$

Multiplying Fractions

Example: $\dfrac{5}{6} \times \dfrac{3}{4} =$

Solution: $\dfrac{5 \times 3}{6 \times 4} = \dfrac{15}{24}$

$\dfrac{15}{24} = \dfrac{5}{8}$

Answer: $\dfrac{5}{8}$

Example: $7 \times \dfrac{4}{5} =$

Solution: $\dfrac{7 \times 4}{1 \times 5} = \dfrac{28}{5}$

$\dfrac{28}{5} = 5\dfrac{3}{5}$

Answer: $5\dfrac{3}{5}$

EXERCISE: Multiply. Write your answers in simplest terms.

1) $\dfrac{1}{2} \times \dfrac{2}{3} =$

2) $\dfrac{3}{5} \times \dfrac{5}{6} =$

3) $\dfrac{7}{8} \times \dfrac{6}{13} =$

4) $\dfrac{2}{9} \times \dfrac{3}{5} =$

5) $\dfrac{6}{7} \times \dfrac{1}{2} =$

6) $\dfrac{3}{11} \times \dfrac{2}{5} =$

7) $\dfrac{2}{7} \times \dfrac{2}{9} =$

8) $\dfrac{1}{6} \times \dfrac{1}{5} =$

9) $\dfrac{5}{11} \times \dfrac{1}{4} =$

10) $\dfrac{1}{6} \times \dfrac{2}{9} =$

11) $\dfrac{5}{6} \times \dfrac{1}{4} =$

12) $\dfrac{3}{11} \times \dfrac{2}{12} =$

13) $\dfrac{4}{5} \times \dfrac{2}{9} =$

14) $\dfrac{4}{7} \times \dfrac{1}{8} =$

15) $\dfrac{3}{16} \times \dfrac{13}{21} =$

16) $\dfrac{5}{21} \times \dfrac{7}{10} =$

17) $\dfrac{5}{24} \times \dfrac{3}{13} =$

18) $\dfrac{6}{28} \times \dfrac{7}{12} =$

19) $\dfrac{2}{3} \times \dfrac{5}{6} =$

20) $\dfrac{12}{21} \times \dfrac{7}{8} =$

21) $\dfrac{13}{32} \times \dfrac{8}{26} =$

22) $\dfrac{24}{25} \times \dfrac{5}{16} =$

23) $\dfrac{1}{12} \times \dfrac{2}{7} =$

24) $\dfrac{2}{17} \times \dfrac{3}{4} =$

25) $\dfrac{10}{13} \times \dfrac{39}{100} =$

26) $\dfrac{12}{18} \times \dfrac{9}{32} =$

27) $\dfrac{2}{15} \times \dfrac{45}{50} =$

28) $\dfrac{5}{11} \times \dfrac{55}{75} =$

29) $\dfrac{4}{5} \times \dfrac{2}{13} =$

30) $\dfrac{2}{11} \times \dfrac{3}{10} =$

31) $\dfrac{3}{14} \times \dfrac{28}{30} =$

32) $\dfrac{7}{13} \times \dfrac{39}{63} =$

33) $\dfrac{24}{36} \times \dfrac{1}{3} =$

REVIEW OF BASIC SKILLS 20

Multiplying Mixed Numbers

Example: $\quad 3\dfrac{2}{3} \times 1\dfrac{1}{2} =$

Solution: $\quad 3\dfrac{2}{3} \times 1\dfrac{1}{2} = \quad \leftarrow$ Change to improper fractions.

$$\dfrac{11}{{}_1 3} \times \dfrac{\overset{1}{\cancel{3}}}{2} = \dfrac{11}{2}$$

$$\dfrac{11}{2} = 5\dfrac{1}{2}$$

EXERCISE: Multiply these mixed numbers. Write your answers in simplest terms.

1) $\quad 2\dfrac{1}{2} \times \dfrac{1}{3} =$

2) $\quad \dfrac{1}{2} \times 1\dfrac{1}{5} =$

3) $\quad \dfrac{2}{7} \times 1\dfrac{1}{3} =$

4) $\quad \dfrac{1}{5} \times 1\dfrac{1}{7} =$

5) $\quad 3\dfrac{1}{5} \times \dfrac{3}{4} =$

6) $\quad 5\dfrac{2}{3} \times \dfrac{1}{5} =$

7) $\quad \dfrac{5}{7} \times 2\dfrac{3}{8} =$

8) $\quad 1\dfrac{1}{2} \times \dfrac{15}{18} =$

9) $\quad 4\dfrac{5}{7} \times \dfrac{7}{11} =$

10) $\quad 2\dfrac{3}{5} \times 1\dfrac{1}{5} =$

11) $\quad 2\dfrac{3}{7} \times 2\dfrac{1}{2} =$

12) $\quad 5\dfrac{1}{7} \times 2\dfrac{1}{5} =$

13) $\quad 5\dfrac{1}{6} \times 1\dfrac{1}{5} =$

14) $\quad 1\dfrac{5}{6} \times 1\dfrac{1}{3} =$

15) $\quad 1\dfrac{2}{7} \times 2\dfrac{1}{8} =$

16) $\quad 6\dfrac{1}{2} \times 2\dfrac{3}{4} =$

17) $\quad 2\dfrac{2}{5} \times 1\dfrac{3}{4} =$

18) $\quad 4\dfrac{1}{2} \times 1\dfrac{1}{4} =$

19) $\quad 3\dfrac{3}{7} \times 2\dfrac{1}{3} =$

20) $\quad 5\dfrac{2}{9} \times 1\dfrac{1}{8} =$

21) $\quad 5\dfrac{1}{4} \times 2\dfrac{1}{7} =$

22) $\quad 6\dfrac{2}{5} \times 1\dfrac{1}{7} =$

23) $\quad 13\dfrac{1}{3} \times 2\dfrac{1}{4} =$

24) $\quad 1\dfrac{5}{9} \times 1\dfrac{3}{4} =$

25) $\quad 3\dfrac{2}{5} \times 2\dfrac{2}{4} =$

26) $\quad 5\dfrac{2}{5} \times 1\dfrac{1}{9} =$

27) $\quad 5\dfrac{1}{3} \times 1\dfrac{1}{8} =$

28) $\quad 5\dfrac{3}{9} \times 1\dfrac{1}{6} =$

29) $\quad 1\dfrac{2}{8} \times 3\dfrac{1}{2} =$

30) $\quad 3\dfrac{1}{2} \times 5\dfrac{1}{6} =$

31) $\quad 2\dfrac{4}{5} \times 2\dfrac{1}{7} =$

32) $\quad 4\dfrac{1}{5} \times 1\dfrac{5}{7} =$

33) $\quad 3\dfrac{7}{8} \times 1\dfrac{1}{2} =$

Dividing Fractions

Example: $\dfrac{4}{7} \div \dfrac{1}{2} =$

Solution: $\dfrac{4}{7} \div \dfrac{1}{2} =$ ← Invert the divisor. Then multiply.

$\dfrac{4}{7} \times \dfrac{2}{1} = \dfrac{8}{7}$

$\dfrac{8}{7} = 1\dfrac{1}{7}$ *Answer:* $1\dfrac{1}{7}$

EXERCISE: Divide. Write your answers in simplest terms.

1) $\dfrac{2}{5} \div \dfrac{2}{7} =$

2) $\dfrac{5}{6} \div \dfrac{1}{3} =$

3) $\dfrac{2}{7} \div \dfrac{1}{8} =$

4) $\dfrac{4}{5} \div \dfrac{1}{6} =$

5) $\dfrac{2}{7} \div \dfrac{5}{6} =$

6) $\dfrac{3}{8} \div \dfrac{1}{2} =$

7) $\dfrac{4}{5} \div \dfrac{5}{6} =$

8) $\dfrac{8}{9} \div \dfrac{4}{5} =$

9) $\dfrac{5}{6} \div \dfrac{2}{5} =$

10) $\dfrac{5}{11} \div \dfrac{2}{22} =$

11) $\dfrac{8}{11} \div \dfrac{5}{11} =$

12) $\dfrac{5}{12} \div \dfrac{5}{6} =$

13) $\dfrac{3}{8} \div \dfrac{5}{12} =$

14) $\dfrac{2}{11} \div \dfrac{3}{22} =$

15) $\dfrac{8}{13} \div \dfrac{24}{26} =$

16) $\dfrac{3}{9} \div \dfrac{1}{5} =$

17) $\dfrac{11}{12} \div \dfrac{24}{30} =$

18) $\dfrac{5}{7} \div \dfrac{48}{49} =$

19) $\dfrac{1}{2} \div \dfrac{5}{7} =$

20) $\dfrac{5}{7} \div \dfrac{5}{14} =$

21) $\dfrac{8}{9} \div \dfrac{3}{6} =$

22) $\dfrac{3}{4} \div \dfrac{6}{7} =$

23) $\dfrac{13}{14} \div \dfrac{3}{7} =$

24) $\dfrac{8}{15} \div \dfrac{2}{5} =$

25) $\dfrac{1}{2} \div \dfrac{1}{2} =$

26) $\dfrac{2}{3} \div \dfrac{1}{7} =$

27) $\dfrac{3}{7} \div \dfrac{15}{21} =$

28) $\dfrac{5}{10} \div \dfrac{2}{6} =$

29) $\dfrac{4}{7} \div \dfrac{5}{14} =$

30) $\dfrac{2}{3} \div \dfrac{14}{21} =$

31) $\dfrac{18}{20} \div \dfrac{15}{40} =$

32) $\dfrac{22}{27} \div \dfrac{11}{18} =$

33) $\dfrac{16}{30} \div \dfrac{8}{15} =$

R E V I E W   O F   B A S I C   S K I L L S   2 2

Dividing Mixed Numbers

Example: $2\dfrac{3}{4} \div 3\dfrac{1}{3} =$

Solution: $2\dfrac{3}{4} \div 3\dfrac{1}{3} =$ ← Rename mixed numbers as improper fractions.

$\dfrac{11}{4} \div \dfrac{10}{3} =$ ← Invert the divisor and multiply.

$\dfrac{11}{4} \times \dfrac{3}{10} = \dfrac{33}{40}$ *Answer:* $\dfrac{33}{40}$

EXERCISE: Divide. Write your answers in simplest terms.

1) $1\dfrac{1}{2} \div \dfrac{1}{2} =$

2) $3\dfrac{2}{3} \div \dfrac{1}{9} =$

3) $1\dfrac{1}{5} \div \dfrac{2}{5} =$

4) $2\dfrac{1}{6} \div \dfrac{3}{12} =$

5) $\dfrac{3}{12} \div 3\dfrac{1}{6} =$

6) $\dfrac{13}{15} \div 1\dfrac{3}{5} =$

7) $1\dfrac{2}{5} \div \dfrac{14}{15} =$

8) $3\dfrac{1}{2} \div \dfrac{5}{6} =$

9) $1\dfrac{1}{2} \div 1\dfrac{2}{5} =$

10) $\dfrac{1}{2} \div 1\dfrac{1}{2} =$

11) $1\dfrac{1}{12} \div 2\dfrac{1}{6} =$

12) $2\dfrac{2}{3} \div 3\dfrac{5}{9} =$

13) $2\dfrac{1}{2} \div 3\dfrac{1}{7} =$

14) $1\dfrac{5}{7} \div \dfrac{6}{7} =$

15) $2\dfrac{5}{8} \div \dfrac{21}{24} =$

16) $3\dfrac{5}{7} \div \dfrac{13}{14} =$

17) $5\dfrac{2}{5} \div \dfrac{3}{4} =$

18) $4\dfrac{1}{3} \div \dfrac{26}{27} =$

19) $5\dfrac{3}{7} \div \dfrac{1}{3} =$

20) $3\dfrac{2}{9} \div \dfrac{1}{8} =$

21) $5\dfrac{2}{5} \div \dfrac{9}{10} =$

22) $8\dfrac{2}{3} \div \dfrac{1}{7} =$

23) $6\dfrac{1}{7} \div \dfrac{7}{18} =$

24) $5\dfrac{1}{5} \div 1\dfrac{1}{2} =$

25) $2\dfrac{3}{4} \div 1\dfrac{1}{6} =$

26) $1\dfrac{1}{7} \div 1\dfrac{1}{6} =$

27) $1\dfrac{1}{8} \div 1\dfrac{1}{9} =$

28) $13\dfrac{2}{3} \div \dfrac{1}{9} =$

29) $3\dfrac{2}{3} \div \dfrac{22}{27} =$

30) $3\dfrac{6}{7} \div 1\dfrac{1}{4} =$

31) $5\dfrac{2}{7} \div 7\dfrac{2}{5} =$

32) $2\dfrac{1}{6} \div 1\dfrac{1}{2} =$

33) $1\dfrac{1}{12} \div 2\dfrac{1}{6} =$

Adding Mixed Numbers with Like Denominators

Example: $3\frac{2}{7} + 1\frac{3}{7} =$

Solution: $3\frac{2}{7}$

$+\ 1\frac{3}{7}$

_____

$4\frac{5}{7}$

Step 1:	Write in the vertical form.
Step 2:	Add the numerators.
	$2 + 3 = 5$
Step 3:	Keep the denominator.
Step 4:	Add the whole numbers.

Answer: $4\frac{5}{7}$

EXERCISE: Add. Write your answers in simplest terms.

1) $\frac{2}{5} + \frac{2}{5}$

2) $\frac{5}{7} + \frac{1}{7}$

3) $\frac{8}{12} + \frac{3}{12}$

4) $\frac{5}{8} + \frac{1}{8}$

5) $\frac{2}{7} + \frac{5}{7}$

6) $\frac{8}{11} + \frac{4}{11}$

7) $1\frac{1}{6} + 2\frac{3}{6}$

8) $2\frac{5}{8} + \frac{1}{8}$

9) $5\frac{3}{10} + \frac{2}{10}$

10) $5\frac{1}{6} + \frac{1}{6}$

11) $8\frac{1}{12} + \frac{3}{12}$

12) $5\frac{1}{6} + \frac{3}{6}$

13) $8\frac{5}{11} + 1\frac{2}{11}$

14) $9\frac{1}{10} + 3\frac{3}{10}$

15) $8\frac{2}{5} + 3\frac{4}{5}$

16) $6\frac{2}{9} + \frac{5}{9}$

17) $8\frac{2}{12} + 6$

18) $11\frac{12}{21} + 2\frac{3}{21}$

19) $5 + 2\frac{1}{7}$

20) $7\frac{1}{7} + 13\frac{1}{7}$

21) $13\frac{12}{21} + 1\frac{3}{21}$

Adding Fractions with Unlike Denominators (24)

Example: $\dfrac{7}{15} + \dfrac{2}{5} =$

Solution:

$$\dfrac{7}{15} = \boxed{\dfrac{7 \times 1}{15 \times 1}} = \dfrac{7}{15}$$

$$+ \dfrac{2}{5} = \boxed{\dfrac{2 \times 3}{5 \times 3}} = + \dfrac{6}{15}$$

$$\dfrac{13}{15}$$

Add the numerators.

Rename the fractions with like denominators.

Adding Mixed Numbers with Unlike Denominators (25)

Example: $5\dfrac{5}{8} + 2\dfrac{7}{12} =$

Solution:

$$5\dfrac{5}{8} \qquad \dfrac{5}{8} = \dfrac{5 \times 3}{8 \times 3} = \dfrac{15}{24} \qquad 5\dfrac{5}{8} = 5\dfrac{15}{24}$$

$$+ 2\dfrac{7}{12} \qquad \dfrac{7}{12} = \dfrac{7 \times 2}{12 \times 2} = \dfrac{14}{24} \qquad + 2\dfrac{7}{12} = 2\dfrac{14}{24}$$

$$7\dfrac{29}{24} = 8\dfrac{5}{24}$$

Rename the fractional portion with like denominators.

Rename $7\dfrac{29}{24}$.

$$7 + \dfrac{29}{24} = 7 + 1\dfrac{5}{24} = 8\dfrac{5}{24}$$

Answer: $8\dfrac{5}{24}$

EXERCISE: Find common denominators and add. Write your answers in simplest terms.

1) $\dfrac{3}{7} + \dfrac{1}{3}$

2) $\dfrac{5}{6} + \dfrac{1}{3}$

3) $\dfrac{8}{12} + \dfrac{1}{8}$

4) $\dfrac{4}{17} + \dfrac{3}{34}$

5) $\dfrac{6}{11} + \dfrac{3}{4}$

6) $\dfrac{8}{15} + \dfrac{1}{6}$

7) $\dfrac{2}{15} + \dfrac{3}{45}$

8) $\dfrac{5}{8} + \dfrac{5}{6}$

9) $\dfrac{7}{9} + \dfrac{5}{27}$

10) $2\dfrac{1}{6} + \dfrac{2}{9}$

11) $12\dfrac{3}{10} + \dfrac{1}{15}$

12) $5\dfrac{6}{72} + \dfrac{1}{8}$

13) $8\dfrac{5}{16} + 2\dfrac{1}{8}$

14) $15\dfrac{2}{17} + 1\dfrac{1}{3}$

15) $26\dfrac{5}{7} + 2\dfrac{4}{21}$

16) $10\dfrac{6}{11} + 2\dfrac{5}{121}$

17) $8\dfrac{3}{36} + 2\dfrac{1}{12}$

18) $9\dfrac{5}{18} + 2\dfrac{5}{54}$

19) $5\dfrac{1}{2} + 2\dfrac{1}{17}$

20) $7\dfrac{3}{36} + 2\dfrac{1}{12}$

21) $3\dfrac{5}{18} + 1\dfrac{5}{54}$

22) $10\dfrac{1}{2} + 12\dfrac{1}{17}$

REVIEW OF BASIC SKILLS 26

Subtracting Mixed Numbers with Like Denominators

Example:

$14 \dfrac{5}{11}$

$- \ 6 \dfrac{2}{11}$

$\rule{3cm}{0.4pt}$

$8 \dfrac{3}{11}$

Step 1:	Subtract 2 from 5.
	$5 - 2 = 3$
Step 2:	Keep the denominator.
Step 3:	Subtract the whole number portions.
	$14 - 6 = 8$

EXERCISE: Subtract. Write your answers in simplest terms.

1) $\dfrac{5}{8} - \dfrac{2}{8}$

2) $\dfrac{6}{13} - \dfrac{2}{13}$

3) $\dfrac{4}{15} - \dfrac{1}{15}$

4) $\dfrac{12}{17} - \dfrac{2}{17}$

5) $\dfrac{8}{9} - \dfrac{5}{9}$

6) $\dfrac{6}{7} - \dfrac{3}{7}$

7) $\dfrac{8}{19} - \dfrac{2}{19}$

8) $2\dfrac{3}{5} - \dfrac{2}{5}$

9) $8\dfrac{7}{8} - \dfrac{3}{8}$

10) $5\dfrac{6}{10} - 4\dfrac{1}{10}$

11) $15\dfrac{12}{13} - 4\dfrac{1}{13}$

12) $7\dfrac{7}{10} - 5\dfrac{2}{10}$

13) $18\dfrac{15}{16} - 5\dfrac{7}{16}$

14) $12\dfrac{5}{8} - 2\dfrac{2}{8}$

15) $17\dfrac{3}{4} - 5\dfrac{2}{4}$

16) $31\dfrac{5}{18} - 2$

17) $39\dfrac{16}{21} - 5\dfrac{6}{21}$

18) $14\dfrac{5}{6} - 2\dfrac{2}{6}$

19) $22\dfrac{3}{10} - 5\dfrac{3}{10}$

20) $9\dfrac{35}{40} - 6\dfrac{10}{40}$

21) $3\dfrac{1}{7} - \dfrac{1}{7}$

Subtracting with Unlike Denominators

Example:

$$18 \frac{2}{3}$$

$$\frac{2}{3} = \frac{2 \times 7}{3 \times 7} = \frac{14}{21}$$

$$- \quad 5 \frac{1}{7}$$

$$\frac{1}{7} = \frac{1 \times 3}{7 \times 3} = \frac{3}{21}$$

$$18 \frac{2}{3} = 18 \frac{14}{21}$$

$$- \quad 5 \frac{1}{7} = 5 \frac{3}{21}$$

$$13 \frac{11}{21}$$

Rename the fractional portions
with like denominators.

Subtract the
numerators and the
whole numbers.

Answer: $\quad 13 \frac{11}{21}$

EXERCISE: Find common denominators and subtract.   Write your answers in simplest terms.

1) $\quad 13 \frac{4}{5} - 5 \frac{2}{3}$

2) $\quad 9 \frac{7}{8} - 3 \frac{1}{3}$

3) $\quad 5 \frac{5}{6} - 2 \frac{1}{3}$

4) $\quad 18 \frac{4}{8} - 5 \frac{2}{24}$

5) $\quad 15 \frac{10}{24} - 5 \frac{1}{6}$

6) $\quad 3 \frac{5}{8} - 1 \frac{2}{6}$

7) $\quad 10 \frac{13}{14} - 3 \frac{1}{2}$

8) $\quad 36 \frac{2}{5} - 5 \frac{1}{6}$

9) $\quad 11 \frac{8}{9} - 5 \frac{2}{8}$

10) $\quad 16 \frac{9}{13} - 2 \frac{2}{3}$

11) $\quad 8 \frac{15}{17} - 2 \frac{2}{3}$

12) $\quad 28 \frac{10}{32} - 5 \frac{1}{8}$

13) $\quad 18 \frac{2}{7} - 16 \frac{1}{28}$

14) $\quad 31 \frac{5}{12} - 4 \frac{3}{48}$

15) $\quad 16 \frac{7}{13} - 5 \frac{2}{39}$

16) $\quad 32 \frac{5}{12} - 8 \frac{2}{24}$

17) $\quad 28 \frac{1}{6} - 3 \frac{1}{9}$

18) $\quad 3 \frac{1}{3} - 1 \frac{1}{7}$

19) $\quad 56 \frac{3}{11} - 5 \frac{1}{9}$

20) $\quad 15 \frac{32}{33} - 8$

21) $\quad 8 \frac{15}{16} - 2 \frac{3}{24}$

REVIEW OF BASIC SKILLS 28

Subtracting with Renaming

Example:

$$12$$

$$- \quad 3\frac{1}{7}$$

Solution:

Step 1: Rename.

$$12 = 11 + 1$$

$$12 = 11 + \frac{7}{7}$$

$$12 = 11\frac{7}{7}$$

Answer: $8\frac{6}{7}$

Step 2: Subtract.

$$12 \qquad = 11\frac{7}{7}$$

$$- \quad 3\frac{1}{7} = 3\frac{1}{7}$$

$$8\frac{6}{7}$$

Example:

$$21\frac{1}{5}$$

$$- \quad 4\frac{3}{5}$$

Solution:

Step 1: Rename.

$$21\frac{1}{5} = 21 + \frac{1}{5}$$

$$= 20 + 1 + \frac{1}{5}$$

$$= 20 + \frac{5}{5} + \frac{1}{5}$$

$$= 20\frac{6}{5}$$

Step 2: Subtract.

$$21\frac{1}{5} = 20\frac{6}{5}$$

$$- \quad 4\frac{3}{5} = 4\frac{3}{5}$$

Answer: $16\frac{3}{5}$

EXERCISE: Find common denominators and subtract. Write your answers in simplest terms.

1) $13\frac{2}{5} - 5\frac{6}{7}$

2) $18\frac{1}{5} - 2\frac{3}{5}$

3) $14\frac{3}{10} - 2\frac{1}{2}$

4) $26\frac{5}{7} - 5\frac{13}{14}$

5) $10\frac{5}{12} - 6\frac{3}{4}$

6) $24\frac{1}{11} - 5\frac{6}{22}$

7) $8\frac{2}{9} - 3\frac{4}{5}$

8) $6\frac{1}{12} - 3\frac{1}{2}$

9) $13\frac{1}{7} - 6\frac{3}{8}$

10) $14 - 2\frac{5}{11}$

11) $28\frac{2}{13} - 6\frac{7}{8}$

12) $12 - 8\frac{3}{7}$

13) $25\frac{5}{6} - 1\frac{9}{10}$

14) $9\frac{2}{15} - 4\frac{4}{5}$

15) $42\frac{1}{5} - 3\frac{3}{8}$

16) $53\frac{6}{9} - 4\frac{17}{18}$

17) $13\frac{5}{11} - 1\frac{21}{22}$

18) $30 - 6\frac{15}{19}$

19) $18\frac{1}{9} - 3\frac{2}{3}$

20) $33\frac{12}{40} - 8\frac{9}{10}$

21) $5\frac{5}{13} - 2\frac{30}{39}$

22) $16\frac{7}{10} - 4\frac{49}{50}$

23) $7\frac{1}{18} - 2\frac{2}{3}$

24) $13\frac{1}{11} - 3\frac{4}{22}$

25) $36 - 8\frac{3}{7}$

26) $13\frac{1}{4} - 5\frac{3}{5}$

27) $27\frac{5}{13} - 6\frac{25}{26}$

28) $14\frac{1}{6} - 3\frac{5}{8}$

29) $18\frac{2}{9} - 6\frac{3}{4}$

30) $6\frac{27}{30} - 5\frac{13}{15}$

31) $7\frac{8}{11} - 1\frac{21}{34}$

32) $6\frac{1}{5} - 4\frac{7}{8}$

33) $4\frac{1}{2} - 2\frac{7}{12}$

34) $16\frac{5}{9} - 3\frac{17}{18}$

35) $14\frac{3}{17} - 2\frac{5}{34}$

36) $2 - 1\frac{5}{11}$

37) $45\frac{4}{9} - 5\frac{4}{5}$

38) $32\frac{5}{16} - 5\frac{15}{32}$

39) $8\frac{3}{14} - 2\frac{6}{7}$

40) $29\frac{1}{10} - 3\frac{10}{15}$

41) $13\frac{5}{16} - 8\frac{23}{24}$

42) $4\frac{2}{7} - 2\frac{4}{5}$

43) $13\frac{15}{35} - 1\frac{6}{7}$

44) $10\frac{2}{3} - 8\frac{8}{9}$

45) $15\frac{11}{20} - 4\frac{4}{5}$

SUPPLEMENTARY PROBLEMS

REVIEW OF BASIC SKILLS 30-31

Identifying Place Value with Decimals (30)

Example: Write the place value of the underlined digits.

1) 23.0671   Hundredths
2) 105.1062   Ten-Thousandths

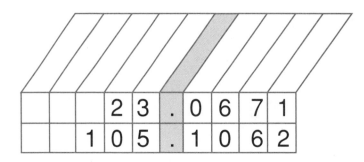

Comparing Decimals (31)

Example: Compare 2.38 and 2.4. Use the symbols < or >.
Solution: Insert zeros to give each decimal the same number of places.
　　　　 1) 2.38 and 2.4
　　　　 2) 2.38 and 2.40 (After inserting a zero.)
　　Since 38 is less than 40, 2.38 < 2.40.

Example: Compare 19.2 and 8.8943.
Solution: Since the whole number 19 is greater than 8, then 19.2 > 8.8943.

EXERCISE: Write the place name for each underlined digit.

1)	35.0̲6	9)	2.08̲35	17)	14.0008̲1
2)	.526̲03	10)	.2850̲1	18)	156.01̲23
3)	5.681̲1̲	11)	12.3005̲2̲	19)	133.0̲1
4)	1.061̲1	12)	52.083̲1	20)	15.01̲911
5)	.5811̲1	13)	.306̲111	21)	1.99̲115
6)	.40101̲5̲	14)	.560̲891	22)	8.5672̲3
7)	.002̲731	15)	1.0065̲1	23)	12.035876̲
8)	2̲76.03	16)	60.00̲79	24)	8̲315.67

Rounding Decimals

Example: Round 2.7017 to the nearest thousandth.

Solution: 2.7017 ← Number (7) to the right of the thousandth place is 5 or more, so add 1 to the thousandths place and drop all digits to the right.

Answer: 2.7017 ≈ 2.702 (≈ means "about equal to.")

Example: Round 8.1649 to the nearest hundredth.

Solution: 8.1649 ← Number (4) to the right of the hundredth place is less than 5, so drop the 4 and 9.

Answer: 8.1649 ≈ 8.16

EXERCISE: Round each decimal to the places named.

		Tenths	Hundredths	Thousandths
1)	2.063	_____	_____	_____
2)	.0891	_____	_____	_____
3)	1.0354	_____	_____	_____
4)	.15454	_____	_____	_____
5)	32.70391	_____	_____	_____
6)	7.63	_____	_____	_____
7)	19.808964	_____	_____	_____
8)	34.00354	_____	_____	_____
9)	2.061155	_____	_____	_____
10)	139.4181891	_____	_____	_____

REVIEW OF BASIC SKILLS 33

Adding Decimals

Example: $23 + .62 + 1.9 =$

Solution:
$$\begin{array}{r} 23. \\ .62 \\ + \ 1.9 \\ \hline 25.52 \end{array}$$
← Line up all the decimal points.

$$\begin{array}{r} 23.00 \\ .62 \\ + \ 1.90 \\ \hline 25.52 \end{array}$$
← Inserting zeros may help.

EXERCISE: Write these problems in vertical form. Then add.

1) $2.3 + 6 + 8.41$
2) $.413 + 9.6 + .2$
3) $17 + .205 + 1.6$
4) $2 + .63 + .5 + 1.1$
5) $3.5 + 8.21 + .006$
6) $8 + .15 + 1.61 + 2$
7) $81.7 + 10.73 + 1.673$
8) $.02 + .603 + 8 + .11$
9) $13.06 + 1.5 + 9 + .41$
10) $2.71 + .031 + 8 + 9.9$
11) $39.4 + 3 + 8.27 + .1$
12) $5 + 8.4 + .07 + 6$
13) $42 + .126 + .1 + .23$
14) $6.28 + .28 + 5.4$
15) $7.6 + 1 + .212$
16) $.561 + 4.7 + 215$
17) $81.4 + 6.7 + 8.41$
18) $50.51 + 2.6 + 9.15$
19) $42.6 + .57 + 23.5$
20) $39.6 + .003 + 1.81$
21) $95.1 + 1.63 + 101.1$
22) $8 + 1.53 + .007$
23) $.203 + .72 + .025$
24) $1.56 + 1.231 + .07$

25) $13 + .92 + 6.7$
26) $83 + 9.6 + 1.305$
27) $5.03 + .607 + .19$
28) $18.95 + 1.4 + .071$
29) $39.9 + 14.62 + 2.3$
30) $2.3 + 1.78 + .663$
31) $8.702 + 3.7 + .63$
32) $3.0101 + .62 + 4$
33) $2.7 + .063 + 1.77$
34) $12.8 + .14 + .03 + 3$
35) $1.9 + 5.621 + .03$
36) $4.7 + .726 + 89.1$
37) $1.7 + 2.31 + .631$
38) $6.7 + .815 + 2$
39) $.37 + 2.9 + 8$
40) $6.09 + .261 + 9.2$
41) $23 + 1.003 + 5.4$
42) $5.21 + .53 + 15.6$
43) $63 + 1.92 + 88.8$
44) $.38 + 7.02 + .115$
45) $5 + .27 + 1.919$
46) $1 + .006 + .0071 + 1.8$
47) $11.001 + 1.1 + 6.27$
48) $3.9 + 1.06 + .081$

R E V I E W   O F   B A S I C   S K I L L S   3 4

Subtracting Decimals

Example: 12 – 1.68 =

Solution:
$$\begin{array}{r} 12.00 \\ -\ 1.68 \\ \hline 10.32 \end{array}$$ ← Line up the decimal points
and insert zeros.

EXERCISE: Write these problems in vertical form. Then subtract.

1)	6.59 – .48 =		26)	53.72 – 1.8 =
2)	36 – 2.3 =		27)	9.01 – .6 =
3)	19.83 – 2.3 =		28)	2.171 – .18 =
4)	33.89 – .32 =		29)	5.6 – .42 =
5)	5.2 – .156 =		30)	2.1 – .8 =
6)	31.4 – 8 =		31)	9 – .62 =
7)	38.5 – 1.67 =		32)	12 – 4.35 =
8)	7.6 – .67 =		33)	1 – .08 =
9)	.091 – .0197 =		34)	.1 – .0356 =
10)	1.1 – .99 =		35)	.35 – .19 =
11)	7.7 – 2.63 =		36)	5.51 – .6 =
12)	36.5 – 1.83 =		37)	19.5 – .34 =
13)	6.7 – 2.34 =		38)	2.81 – .931 =
14)	1.6 – 1.08 =		39)	11.23 – 9.9 =
15)	.89 – .098 =		40)	31.3 – .61 =
16)	2.31 – .9 =		41)	4.35 – .6 =
17)	.011 – .00201 =		42)	.68 – .086 =
18)	.3 – .234 =		43)	.1 – .06 =
19)	1.03 – .89 =		44)	1.63 – .89 =
20)	75 – .108 =		45)	7.5 – 6 =
21)	8.7 – 2.31 =		46)	3 – .4 =
22)	1 – .9 =		47)	5.52 – .66 =
23)	8.3 – .99 =		48)	6 – .9 =
24)	45.1 – .06 =		49)	.32 – .0823 =
25)	.101 – .0982 =		50)	1 – .662 =

REVIEW OF BASIC SKILLS 35

Multiplying Decimals

Example: $.26 \times 1.3 =$

Solution:
$$
\begin{array}{r}
.26 \\
\times\ 1.3 \\
\hline
78 \\
26\ \ \\
\hline
.338
\end{array}
$$

← 2 places plus
← 1 place equals

← 3 places

Example: $.321 \times .002 =$

Solution:
$$
\begin{array}{r}
.321 \\
\times\ \ .002 \\
\hline
.000642
\end{array}
$$

← 3 places plus
← 3 places equals
← 6 places

EXERCISE: Write these problems in vertical form. Then multiply.

1)	$.2 \times .3 =$	19)	$.5 \times 6 =$
2)	$.7 \times 1.2 =$	20)	$1.3 \times .8 =$
3)	$1.9 \times .3 =$	21)	$2.3 \times .5 =$
4)	$2.6 \times 8 =$	22)	$4.3 \times .8 =$
5)	$.26 \times .2 =$	23)	$3.5 \times .7 =$
6)	$.62 \times .3 =$	24)	$.85 \times 3 =$
7)	$.81 \times 1.2 =$	25)	$.26 \times 1.5 =$
8)	$.42 \times 6.3 =$	26)	$1.8 \times .18 =$
9)	$.92 \times .21 =$	27)	$4.8 \times .06 =$
10)	$.65 \times .07 =$	28)	$.31 \times .09 =$
11)	$1.23 \times 1.2 =$	29)	$3.62 \times .05 =$
12)	$.128 \times .52 =$	30)	$.402 \times .11 =$
13)	$5.8 \times .006 =$	31)	$.71 \times .62 =$
14)	$.081 \times .02 =$	32)	$1.62 \times .71 =$
15)	$.96 \times .73 =$	33)	$52.6 \times .36 =$
16)	$8.03 \times .67 =$	34)	$4.2 \times .008 =$
17)	$.126 \times .73 =$	35)	$703 \times .02 =$
18)	$25.3 \times .62 =$	36)	$.91 \times .083 =$

Scientific Notation

Example: Express 2800 in scientific notation.

Solution: $2800 = 2.800 \times 10^3$ ← 3 places

or

2.8×10^3

Example: Express 0.00039 in scientific notation.

Solution: $0.00039 = 3.9 \times 10^{-4}$ ← 4 places

(Use the negative sign ($^{-4}$) when the decimal point is moved to the right.)

EXERCISE: Write these numbers in scientific notation.

1)	3600	23)	510
2)	35,100	24)	8702
3)	46,000	25)	92,300
4)	75,100	26)	18,000
5)	6530	27)	980,000
6)	391,000	28)	5,600,000
7)	1,725,000	29)	7,810,000
8)	5,301,000	30)	1,000,000
9)	87,100,000	31)	45,000,000
10)	267,000,000	32)	9,720,000
11)	100,000	33)	5,300,000,000
12)	1,700,000,000	34)	961,000,000
13)	34,000,000	35)	171,800,000
14)	306.2	36)	48.39
15)	12.721	37)	150.82
16)	.0000623	38)	.0000031
17)	.00002	39)	.000175
18)	.1602	40)	.003
19)	623.05	41)	.00231
20)	.000000005	42)	.000000453
21)	.00000101	43)	.000119
22)	.00663	44)	.0024

Dividing Decimals by Whole Numbers (37)

Example: .168 ÷ 14 =

Solution:

```
   .012
14 ).168
   14
   28
   28
```

Place the decimal point in the quotient directly above the one in the dividend.

Example: 68.6 ÷ 28 =

Solution:

```
    2.45
28 ) 68.60
    56
    126
    112
    140
    140
```

Adding a zero may terminate the answer.

Dividing Decimals by Decimals (38)

Example: 8.04 ÷ .6 =

Solution:

```
    13.4
.6 ) 8.04
    6
    20
    18
    24
    24
```

Step 1: Move the decimal point in the divisor to the right.

Step 2: Move the decimal point in the dividend the same number of places to the right.

Step 3: Divide and bring the decimal point straight up into the quotient.

Renaming Decimals as Fractions (39)

Example: Rename .13 as a fraction.

Solution: $.13 = \frac{13}{100}$

Example: .026 = ?

Solution: $.026 = \frac{26}{1000}$ or $\frac{13}{500}$

Renaming Fractions as Decimals (40)

Example: Rename $\dfrac{13}{25}$ as a decimal.

Solution:

$$\dfrac{13}{25} = \dfrac{13 \times 4}{25 \times 4} = \dfrac{52}{100}$$

Choose a multiplier that will give you a denominator that is a power of 10. (10, 100, 1000, 10000...)

$$= .52 \quad \text{OR}$$

$$25\,\overline{)\,13.00}^{\,.52}$$
$$\underline{125}$$
$$50$$
$$\underline{50}$$

Dividing the numerator by the denominator will also give the decimal equivalent.

EXERCISE: Copy these problems and divide. Rename decimals as fractions.

1)	$4.7 \div 2 =$		22)	$36.8 \div 8 =$
2)	$.78 \div 3 =$		23)	$3.51 \div 9 =$
3)	$1.448 \div .8 =$		24)	$7.23 \div 3 =$
4)	$2.88 \div .9 =$		25)	$2.412 \div .6 =$
5)	$10.2 \div 1.2 =$		26)	$8.32 \div 3.2 =$
6)	$11.55 \div 2.1 =$		27)	$10.44 \div 2.9 =$
7)	$4.545 \div .9 =$		28)	$.159 \div .15 =$
8)	$2.807 \div .7 =$		29)	$.266 \div .07 =$
9)	$.351 \div .09 =$		30)	$2.173 \div 4.1 =$
10)	$4.004 \div .22 =$		31)	$.2412 \div .2 =$
11)	$.777 \div .15 =$		32)	$.644 \div .46 =$
12)	$13.7046 \div .91 =$		33)	$.688 \div 8 =$
13)	$.0615 \div 1.5 =$		34)	$.0066 \div .11 =$
14)	$.00902 \div .41 =$		35)	$1.554 \div .42 =$
15)	$.01952 \div 3.2 =$		36)	$.0858 \div .006 =$
16)	$.00206 \div .002 =$		37)	$.1242 \div .06 =$
17)	$32.92 \div .4 =$		38)	$21.7124 \div 6.2 =$
18)	$.12741 \div .31 =$		39)	$7.2024 \div 1.2 =$
19)	$.08833 \div .11 =$		40)	$.6162 \div .15 =$
20)	$.0084 \div .007 =$		41)	$.0693 \div 3.3 =$
21)	$6.2432 \div 1.6 =$		42)	$2.2194 \div 5.4 =$

REVIEW OF BASIC SKILLS 41-46

Solving Proportions (41)

Example: $\dfrac{25}{N} = \dfrac{5}{6}$

Solution: $\dfrac{25}{N} = \dfrac{5}{6}$

$$5 \times N = 25 \times 6$$
$$5 \times N = 150$$
$$N = 150 \div 5$$
$$N = 30$$

Changing Percents to Decimals (42)

Example: Write 32% as a decimal.
Solution: 32% = .32

Example: Write 6.3% as a decimal.
Solution: 6.3% = .063

> Move the decimal point 2 places to the left and remove the % sign.

Changing Percents to Fractions (43)

Example: Write 45% as a fraction.

Solution: 45% = .45

$$45\% = \dfrac{45}{100}$$

$$45\% = \dfrac{9}{20}$$

Renaming Decimals as Percents (44)

Example: Write .231 as a percent.
Solution: .231 = 23.1%
Move the decimal point 2 places to the right.

Renaming Fractions as Percents (45)

Example: Write $\dfrac{7}{8}$ as a percent.

Solution: First express $\dfrac{7}{8}$ as a decimal.

$$\begin{array}{r} .875 \\ 8\,)\overline{\,7.000} \\ \underline{6\,4} \\ 60 \\ \underline{56} \\ 40 \\ \underline{40} \end{array}$$

$$\dfrac{7}{8} = .875$$
$$= 87.5\% \text{ or } 87\dfrac{1}{2}\%$$

Answer: 87.5%

Finding the Percentage (46)

Example: 23% of 35 is what number?

Solution: $.23 \times 35 = N$
            $8.05 \qquad = N$

EXERCISE A: Find the percentage.

1)   20% of 52 is ____
2)   35% of 60 is ____
3)   70% of 50 is ____
4)   10% of 82 is ____
5)   2% of 39 is ____
6)   5% of 7 is ____
7)   14% of 2.8 is ____
8)   39% of 6 is ____
9)   3% of 4.9 is ____
10)   6% of .42 is ____
11)   18% of 5.6 is ____
12)   56% of 23.5 is ____
13)   7% of .82 is ____
14)   32% of .38 is ____

15)   25% of 75 is ____
16)   62% of 35 is ____
17)   9% of 150 is ____
18)   15% of 20 is ____
19)   26% of 40 is ____
20)   3% of 35 is ____
21)   23% of 5 is ____
22)   19% of 8 is ____
23)   8% of 7.02 is ____
24)   11% of 3.6 is ____
25)   13% of 2.5 is ____
26)   70% of .38 is ____
27)   53% of .72 is ____
28)   6.2% of 32 is ____

EXERCISE B: Find the rate.

1)   ___% of 72 is 1.44
2)   ___% of 350 is 14
3)   ___% of 380 is 34.2
4)   ___% of 2.8 is .42
5)   ___% of 4.5 is .18
6)   ___% of 5.1 is 1.632
7)   ___% of .26 is .1248
8)   ___% of 1.5 is .48
9)   ___% of .03 is .0021
10)   ___% of 1.8 is .09
11)   ___% of 30 is .87
12)   ___% of 80 is 4.96
13)   ___% of 35 is 2.065
14)   ___% of 80 is 7.36

15)   ___% of 90 is 5.4
16)   ___% of 10 is .8
17)   ___% of 320 is 16
18)   ___% of 6.3 is 1.26
19)   ___% of 6.1 is .61
20)   ___% of 5.3 is 2.067
21)   ___% of .41 is .2214
22)   ___% of 4.5 is 1.71
23)   ___% of .9 is .594
24)   ___% of .3 is .0243
25)   ___% of 50 is 2.1
26)   ___% of 53 is 4.823
27)   ___% of 60 is 1.68
28)   ___% of 90 is 6.48

EXERCISE C: Find the base.

1)   6% of ___ is .03
2)   7% of ___ is .021
3)   8% of ___ is .152
4)   15% of ___ is 145.5
5)   23% of ___ is 8.05
6)   4% of ___ is 2.48
7)   3.5% of ___ is 53.2
8)   7% of ___ is .042
9)   15% of ___ is .345
10)   2.3% of ___ is 2.185
11)   .14% of ___ is .0462
12)   .91% of ___ is .5733
13)   .26% of ___ is .0208
14)   .9% of ___ is .0216
15)   28% of ___ is 82.88
16)   235% of ___ is 18.8
17)   110% of ___ is 42.9
18)   .07% of ___ is .0035

19)   9% of ___ is .81
20)   4% of ___ is .52
21)   6% of ___ is 1.68
22)   22% of ___ is 75.02
23)   4% of ___ is 11.2
24)   9% of ___ is 90
25)   5% of ___ is .045
26)   9% of ___ is 0.153
27)   18% of ___ is .0234
28)   4.2% of ___ is 2.646
29)   5.9% of ___ is 11.8
30)   .11% of ___ is .033
31)   20.3% of ___ is 1.827
32)   .5% of ___ is .0025
33)   41% of ___ is 37.843
34)   140% of ___ is 74.2
35)   99% of ___ is 97.02
36)   .06% of ___ is .0078

EXERCISE D: Find the missing numbers.

1) 2% of ___ is .16.
2) 18% of 25 is ___.
3) ___% of 150 is 43.5.
4) 7% of ___ is 1.96.
5) 53% of 69 is ___.
6) ___% of 36 is 3.6.
7) 8% of ___ is 4.48.
8) 17% of 39 is ___.
9) ___% of 32 is 8.
10) 26% of ___ is .676.
11) 52% of 35 is ___.
12) ___% of 8.5 is 1.36.
13) 75% of ___ is 19.65.
14) 30% of 35.4 is ___.
15) ___% of 15.2 is 13.832.
16) 2.8% of 60 is ___.
17) 2.9% of 60 is ___.
18) ___% of 7.7 is .77.
19) 95% of ___ is 9.5.
20) 11% of 19 is ___.
21) ___% of 77.1 is 21.588.
22) 15% of ___ is 5.4.
23) .07% of 276 is ___.
24) ___% of 378 is .756.
25) .08% of ___ is .0312.

26) 6% of 2.8 is ___.
27) 32% of ___ is 16.96.
28) ___% of 16 is .8.
29) 43% of ___ is 13.76.
30) 9% of 156 is ___.
31) 92% of ___ is 184.
32) ___% of 100 is 3.9.
33) 19% of 56 is ___.
34) 75% of ___ is 28.5.
35) ___% of 81 is 7.29.
36) 80% of 30 is ___.
37) 35% of ___ is 3.185.
38) ___% of 30 is 5.4.
39) 28% of 6.5 is ___.
40) 20% of ___ is 6.44.
41) ___% of 60 is 3.18.
42) 4.3% of 50 is ___.
43) 13% of ___ is .507.
44) ___% of 31 is 1.736.
45) 62% of 24 is ___.
46) 3.4% of ___ is 2.754.
47) ___% of 37 is 13.69.
48) 29% of 300 is ___.
49) .25% of ___ is .0375.
50) ___% of 4.2 is .21.

APPENDIX

BASIC Computer Programming

Each chapter contains a computer exercise usually in the form of a basic program. These programs are written in the BASIC (Beginners All-purpose Symbolic Instruction Code) programming language and should run with little difficulty. Your computer science teacher will get you started with BASIC. Follow these steps:

1) Turn on the computer and monitor and adjust the contrast on the monitor if needed.

2) Access BASIC programming under the supervision of your computer science teacher.

3) Enter the program found in the chapter's computer exercise by typing each line exactly as it is printed.

4) Remember to use the ENTER or RETURN key after the completion of each line.

5) Check the program for accuracy by retyping any lines that may be incorrect.

6) Run the program by typing the command RUN.

The programs should run with little trouble. However, it may be necessary to replace HOME for CLS.

```
Use HOME for CLS
        or
    CLS for HOME
```

Each computer program is designed as an enrichment activity. Generally the programs occur where the computations are cumbersome or in some way difficult to compute by hand. The programs do not teach any new mathematics and may be ignored without loss of mathematical content. However, their use is encouraged so that students will investigate how the computer program accomplishes the same task as they do with their mathematical computation. Additionally, it should be noted that student interest is often increased by the use of computers.

GLOSSARY

A

Add — to combine numbers into a sum or total

Addend — one of the numbers being added

Addition — one of the four basic arithmetic operations

Advance — to move forward

Annual — yearly; happening once a year

Area — amount of space inside a shape

Assist — in baseball, a defensive play by a fielder that helps a teammate to make a putout

Average — is the number obtained by dividing the sum of two or more quantities by the number of quantities; the arithmetic mean

B

Balance — the difference between the amount of money one owes and the amount one has

Bar graph — a pictorial way to compare amounts using rectangles

Base — amount that a percent is taken of

Baserunning average — ratio of stolen bases to attempted steals

Batting average — a ratio of hits to at bats

Beneficiary — a person who receives the face value of an insurance policy

Budget — a plan for managing money

C

Calculate — to get an answer by adding, subtracting, multiplying, or dividing

Calculation — answer found by adding, subtracting, multiplying, or dividing

Calisthenics — exercises to develop a strong, trim body

Calorie — unit of measure of the energy in food; the amount of heat needed to raise the temperature of one gram of water one degree Centigrade

Celsius — a type of thermometer on which 0 degrees is the freezing point and 100 degrees is the boiling point of water

Centimeter — a unit of measure equal to 1/100 meter

Circle — a plane figure all of whose points are the same distance from the center

Circle graph — pictorial way to show comparisons by using the segments of a circle

Clockwise — in the direction in which the hands of a clock rotate

Colon — a mark of punctuation (:) used between the hour and the minutes of written time

Compare — to look for likenesses and differences; to examine two numbers to determine which is larger

Compound interest — interest computed on principal and interest

Compute — to calculate or figure out

Construct — to draw so as to meet the specified requirements

Construction class — type of house

Consume — to use; to eat or drink up

Consumption — using up

Conversion — an exchange for something equal in value; switching from one unit to another

Conversion factor — a number you multiply a measurement by to obtain equivalent measurement with a different unit of measure

Convert — to change from one form to another

Coverage — the area of wall that a can of paint is supposed to cover, usually measured in square feet

Credit — the right to buy now and to pay later

Cubic — having the shape of a cube; the volume of a cube whose length, width, and depth each measure the same

Currency — money

D

Deal — (dealt) to hand playing cards one by one to the players

Decimal — a fraction with a denominator of 10, or a power of 10 written with a decimal point

Decimal places — positions to the right of the decimal point

Deck — a pack of playing cards

Deductions — money withheld from gross pay for taxes, insurance, dues, etc.

Degree — 1/360th of a circle

Denominator — the part of the fraction below the line that tells how many parts there are in all

Dependent — a person who depends on someone else for support

Diameter — distance across a circle

Dice — (*plural:* **die**) small cubes of bone, plastic, etc., marked on each side with from one to six spots and used usually in pairs

Dice sum — the total points shown on two or more dice

Difference — the amount remaining when one part or number is taken away from another; the answer to a subtraction problem

Digit — any numeral from 0 to 9

Discount — the amount taken off the usual price

Discount rate — the percent that the price is reduced

Divide — to separate into equal parts by a divisor

Dividend — the number to be divided

Division — one of the four basic arithmetic operations

Divisor — the number you are dividing by

Double roll — an amount of wallpaper that covers twice the wall area as a single roll

Double time — payment of two times the hourly rate

Draw — to get or pick at random

E

Earned run average — nine times the earned runs divided by the innings pitched; the measure of how many runs a pitcher allows in a game

Elapse — to slip by; to pass

Elapsed time — the difference between the time at the start and the time at the end of an event

Endowment insurance — insurance where premium is paid for a period and then the face value is paid to the insured

Equivalent — a thing that is equal to another in a particular way

Error — in baseball, any misplay in fielding a ball that allows a player who should have been out to reach a base safely or remain at bat, or that permits a runner to advance

Estimate — to give a reasonable or approximate number; to make a general but careful guess of the number, size, or value of something

Event — outcome

Expect — to look forward to

Experimental — based on trials or tests

Exponent — a small figure or symbol placed at the upper right of another figure or symbol to show how many times the latter is to be multiplied by itself

Express — to write or say

F

Fabric — a material made from fibers or threads by weaving, knitting, etc.

Fabric guide — a chart showing the amount of material needed to make garments of different sizes

Face value — the worth printed or written on a bill, bond, etc.

Factor — numbers that when multiplied together form a product; number being multiplied

Fahrenheit — a type of thermometer on which 32 degrees is the freezing point and 212 degrees is the boiling point of water

Field — in baseball, to stop or catch or to catch and throw a ball in play

Fielding percentage — ratio of assists and putouts to total chances

Finance charge — cost of borrowing money; money paid for the use of money; the rate of payment, expressed as a percentage per unit of time

Foot — a measure of length, equal to 12 inches

Formula — a rule or method for doing something

Fraction — a number with a numerator and a denominator (i.e., 1/2); a rational number

Frame — in bowling, any of the divisions of a game in which all ten pins are set up anew

G

Gallon — a liquid measure equal to 4 quarts

Games back — the sum of the difference of wins and losses between a team and the first place team divided by two

Geometric — formed of straight lines, triangles, circles, etc., as a pattern

Gram — a unit of measure in the metric system

Graph — a pictorial way to display information

Gross — total; with no deductions

Gross pay — pay before deductions

Gymnastics — exercises that develop and train the body and the muscles

H

Height — the distance from the top to the bottom

Hexagon — a plane figure with six angles and six sides

Hourly — happening or done every hour or during the hour

I

Improper fraction — a fraction whose numerator is equal to or greater than the denominator

Increase — to make larger

Inspect — to look at carefully

Insurance — coverage by a contract in which one party guarantees another against loss for a sum of money

Interest — amount paid for the use of money; money paid by a borrower for the borrowed money

Interest rate — percent paid or charged for the use of money

Invert — to change to the direct opposite

K

Kilowatt — a unit of electrical power

L

Lend — to make a loan or loans

Length — the distance from end to end

Liability — insurance that protects the owner against claims resulting from an accident that is his or her fault

Line segment — a part of a line; a line with defined end points

List price — the usual price of an item

Loan — money given to a borrower that is to be returned at a given time with interest

M

Macrame — a coarse fringe or lace of thread or cord knotted into designs

Major medical insurance — insurance to cover larger medical expenses

Meter — an instrument for measuring and recording the quantity or rate of flow of gas, electricity, water, etc., passing through it

Metered parking space — a parking space where you must put money in a parking meter

Mileage — number of miles traveled

Mixed number — a number consisting of a whole number and a fraction

Multiplication — one of the four basic arithmetic operations

Multiply — to use the short way of adding one number to itself the number of times indicated by another number

N

Numeral — a symbol or symbols representing a number

Numerator — the part of the fraction that is above the line, that tells how many parts are used

Nutrient — something that provides nourishment

O

Odometer — an instrument for measuring the distance traveled by a vehicle

Ordinary life insurance — insurance where payments are made as long as the insured is alive

Outcome — result

Overtime — time beyond the estimated limit

P

Partial product — answer obtained when one factor is multiplied by a digit in the other factor

Payment — the giving of what is due, as for goods or services

Per — each

Percent — number per hundred

Percentage — a given part or amount in every hundred; the part in a percent problem

Perimeter — the distance around all the sides of a polygon

Place value — the position of a number, as in noting decimals; worth based upon position in a numeral

Polygon — a closed plane figure with three or more sides and angles; especially one with more than four sides and angles

Possible outcome — results that can happen

Possibilities — outcomes that can occur

Pounds — unit of measure

Predict — to state what will happen

Premium — amount paid for insurance

Premium chart — list of amounts to be paid for insurance

Principal — amount of a loan or a deposit

Prism — a transparent, three-sided bar used to separate light into the colors of the rainbow

Probability — the ratio of the number of times a particular event can occur to the total number of likely events involved; the chances that an outcome will happen

Probability tree — a diagram showing all possible outcomes

Procedure — the order of steps to be followed

Product — the answer obtained when two or more numbers are multiplied together; the answer to a multiplication problem

Proper fraction — a fraction in which the numerator is less than the denominator

Proportion — a relationship between four numbers, in which the quotient of the first two is the same the last two

Protractor — an instrument in the form of a half-circle marked with degrees, for plotting and measuring angles

Putout — in baseball, a play in which the batter or runner is retired

Q

Quart — a unit of measure

Quarterly — happening at regular intervals four times a year

Quotient — the answer obtained when one number is divided by another; the answer to a division problem

R

Radius — a straight line from the center to the outside of a circle

Rate — percent; a comparison in the form of a ratio

Rate factor — an amount of one thing in relation to units of another thing, as miles per hour

Ratio — the relationship in quantity, amount, or size between two or more things

Recipe — directions for making something

Rectangle — any four-sided plane figure with four right angles

Rectangular — shaped like a rectangle

Regroup — to reorganize; to group again

Remainder — the amount left over when dividing

Rename — to express in another form equal to the original (i.e., 1 hour = 60 minutes)

Rent — payment for the temporary use of a house, land, etc., made at regular times by the user to the owner

Repeat — to do or to make again

Replacement cost — the cost to replace insured property

Round — to express as a round number (500 is a round number for 498)

Round up — to round to the next highest number

Rummy — any of certain card games in which the object is to match cards into sets of the same denomination or sequences of the same suit

S

Sacrifice outs — outs made to advance base runners

Salary — a fixed amount of money paid to a worker on a regular basis, such as weekly or monthly, for work done

Sale price — reduced price of an item

Sales tax — a tax on sales or services, added to the price paid by a customer

Scale — ratio of the real size of an object or area to the map size

Scale drawing — a picture that shows relative sizes of real objects

Scientific notation — a system in which numbers are expressed as products of a number between 1 and 10 multiplied and a power of 10 (i.e., $26,000 = 2.6 \times 10^4$)

Score — the number of points made in a game by one team

Shuffle — to mix playing cards so as to change their order

Simple interest — interest computed on principal only

Simplify — to make less complex; to reduce to simplest terms

Simplest terms (or **simplest form**) — a fraction where the numerator and the denominator have no factors other than one in common

Slugging percentage — ratio of total bases to at bats

Spare — in bowling, a knocking down of all the pins with two rolls of the ball

Speedometer — an instrument that measures how fast a car is traveling

Square — a plane figure having four equal sides and four right angles

Square units — units used to measure area, such as square feet, square inches, or square yards

Standard — regulation

Statistics — facts collected and arranged so as to show certain information

Strike — in bowling, the act of knocking down all ten pins on one roll of the ball

Subtract — to take away one amount from another

Subtraction — one of the four basic arithmetic operations

Suit — any of the four sets of thirteen playing cards, each in a pack

Sum — the total when everything is added together; the answer to an addition problem

Surface area — the amount of space on a flat surface

Symbol — a character that stands for something else

T

Tax — a payment to the government

Term insurance — insurance where payments and insurance last for a fixed amount of time

Time — duration of a loan or deposit

Time and one-half — payment of 1.5 times the hourly rate for work

Total — answer to an addition problem

Trapezoid — a plane figure with four sides, only two of which are parallel

U

Unit — any fixed amount, quantity, etc., used as a standard

V

Value — the worth of something (in money or goods) at a certain time

Verify — to prove to be true by evidence

Vertical — upright, straight up or down

Volume — the amount of space occupied in three dimensions

W

Walk — to gain first base because four balls are pitched

Watt — a unit of electrical power

Weekly — happening once a week or every week

Whole number — zero or a multiple of 1; 0, 1, 2, 3, etc.

Width — the distance from side to side

Won-lost percentage — ratio of wins to games played

Y

Yard — a measure of length, equal to 3 feet or 36 inches

Yearly — happening once a year or every year

INDEX